Connected  Mathematics™

Say It with Symbols

Algebraic Reasoning

Teacher's Guide

Glenda Lappan
James T. Fey
William M. Fitzgerald
Susan N. Friel
Elizabeth Difanis Phillips

PEARSON
Prentice
Hall

Glenview, Illinois
Needham, Massachusetts
Upper Saddle River, New Jersey

Connected Mathematics™ was developed at Michigan State University with financial support from the Michigan State University Office of the Provost, Computing and Technology, and the College of Natural Science.

This material is based upon work supported by the National Science Foundation under Grant No. MDR 9150217.

This project was supported, in part,
by the
National Science Foundation
Opinions expressed are those of the authors
and not necessarily those of the Foundation

The Michigan State University authors and administration have agreed that all MSU royalties arising from this publication will be devoted to purposes supported by the Department of Mathematics and the MSU Mathematics Education Enrichment Fund.

Photo Acknowledgements: 6 © Mike Valeri/FPG International; 7 © Jeff Greenberg/Peter Arnold, Inc.; 11 © Medford Taylor/Superstock, Inc.; 14 © Mike Greenlar/The Image Works; 17 © Superstock; 24 © Gale Zucker/Stock, Boston; 29 © Cathlyn Melloan/Tony Stone Images; 41 © Elizabeth Crews/The Image Works; 48 © Peter Menzel/Stock, Boston

PEARSON
Prentice
Hall

ISBN 0-13-180802-8
4 5 6 7 8 9 10   07 06 05

Patricia Wagner
Holmes Middle School

Greg Williams
Gundry Elementary School

Lansing

Susan Bissonette
Waverly Middle School

Kathy Booth
Waverly East Intermediate School

Carole Campbell
Waverly East Intermediate School

Gary Gillespie
Waverly East Intermediate School

Denise Kehren
Waverly Middle School

Virginia Larson
Waverly East Intermediate School

Kelly Martin
Waverly Middle School

Laurie Metevier
Waverly East Intermediate School

Craig Paksi
Waverly East Intermediate School

Tony Pecoraro
Waverly Middle School

Helene Rewa
Waverly East Intermediate School

Arnold Stiefel
Waverly Middle School

Portland

Bill Carlton
Portland Middle School

Kathy Dole
Portland Middle School

Debby Flate
Portland Middle School

Yvonne Grant
Portland Middle School

Terry Keusch
Portland Middle School

John Manzini
Portland Middle School

Mary Parker
Portland Middle School

Scott Sandborn
Portland Middle School

Shepherd

Steve Brant
Shepherd Middle School

Marty Brock
Shepherd Middle School

Cathy Church
Shepherd Middle School

Ginny Crandall
Shepherd Middle School

Craig Ericksen
Shepherd Middle School

Natalie Hackney
Shepherd Middle School

Bill Hamilton
Shepherd Middle School

Julie Salisbury
Shepherd Middle School

Sturgis

Sandra Allen
Eastwood Elementary School

Margaret Baker
Eastwood Elementary School

Steven Baker
Eastwood Elementary School

Keith Barnes
Sturgis Middle School

Wilodean Beckwith
Eastwood Elementary School

Darcy Bird
Eastwood Elementary School

Bill Dickey
Sturgis Middle School

Ellen Eisele
Sturgis Middle School

James Hoelscher
Sturgis Middle School

Richard Nolan
Sturgis Middle School

J. Hunter Raiford
Sturgis Middle School

Cindy Sprowl
Eastwood Elementary School

Leslie Stewart
Eastwood Elementary School

Connie Sutton
Eastwood Elementary School

Traverse City

Maureen Bauer
Interlochen Elementary School

Ivanka Berskshire
East Junior High School

Sarah Boehm
Courtade Elementary School

Marilyn Conklin
Interlochen Elementary School

Nancy Crandall
Blair Elementary School

Fran Cullen
Courtade Elementary School

Eric Dreier
Old Mission Elementary School

Lisa Dzierwa
Cherry Knoll Elementary School

Ray Fouch
West Junior High School

Ed Hargis
Willow Hill Elementary School

Richard Henry
West Junior High School

Dessie Hughes
Cherry Knoll Elementary School

Ruthanne Kladder
Oak Park Elementary School

Bonnie Knapp
West Junior High School

Sue Laisure
Sabin Elementary School

Stan Malaski
Oak Park Elementary School

Jody Meyers
Sabin Elementary School

Marsha Myles
East Junior High School

Mary Beth O'Neil
Traverse Heights Elementary School

Jan Palkowski
East Junior High School

Karen Richardson
Old Mission Elementary School

Kristin Sak
Bertha Vos Elementary School

Mary Beth Schmitt
East Junior High School

Mike Schrotenboer
Norris Elementary School

Gail Smith
Willow Hill Elementary School

Karrie Tufts
Eastern Elementary School

Mike Wilson
East Junior High School

Tom Wilson
West Junior High School

Minnesota

Minneapolis

Betsy Ford
Northeast Middle School

New York

East Elmhurst

Allison Clark
Louis Armstrong Middle School

Dorothy Hershey
Louis Armstrong Middle School

J. Lewis McNeece
Louis Armstrong Middle School

Rossana Perez
Louis Armstrong Middle School

Merna Porter
Louis Armstrong Middle School

Marie Turini
Louis Armstrong Middle School

North Carolina

Durham

Everly Broadway
Durham Public Schools

Thomas Carson
Duke School for Children

Mary Hebrank
Duke School for Children

Bill O'Connor
Duke School for Children

Ruth Pershing
Duke School for Children

Peter Reichert
Duke School for Children

Elizabeth City

Rita Banks
Elizabeth City Middle School

Beth Chaundry
Elizabeth City Middle School

Amy Cuthbertson
Elizabeth City Middle School

Deni Dennison
Elizabeth City Middle School

Jean Gray
Elizabeth City Middle School

John McMenamin
Elizabeth City Middle School

Nicollette Nixon
Elizabeth City Middle School

Malinda Norfleet
Elizabeth City Middle School

Joyce O'Neal
Elizabeth City Middle School

Clevie Sawyer
Elizabeth City Middle School

Juanita Shannon
Elizabeth City Middle School

Terry Thorne
Elizabeth City Middle School

Rebecca Wardour
Elizabeth City Middle School

Leora Winslow
Elizabeth City Middle School

Franklinton

Susan Haywood
Franklinton Elementary School

Clyde Melton
Franklinton Elementary School

Louisburg

Lisa Anderson
Terrell Lane Middle School

Jackie Frazier
Terrell Lane Middle School

Pam Harris
Terrell Lane Middle School

Ohio

Toledo

Bonnie Bias
Hawkins Elementary School

Marsha Jackish
Hawkins Elementary School

Lee Jagodzinski
DeVeaux Junior High School

Norma J. King
Old Orchard Elementary School

Margaret McCready
Old Orchard Elementary School

Carmella Morton
DeVeaux Junior High School

Karen C. Rohrs
Hawkins Elementary School

Marie Sahloff
DeVeaux Junior High School

L. Michael Vince
McTigue Junior High School

Brenda D. Watkins
Old Orchard Elementary School

Oregon

Canby

Sandra Kralovec
Ackerman Middle School

Portland

Roberta Cohen
Catlin Gabel School

David Ellenberg
Catlin Gabel School

Sara Normington
Catlin Gabel School

Karen Scholte-Arce
Catlin Gabel School

West Linn

Marge Burack
Wood Middle School

Tracy Wygant
Athey Creek Middle School

Pennsylvania

Pittsburgh

Sheryl Adams
Reizenstein Middle School

Sue Barie
Frick International Studies Academy

Suzie Berry
Frick International Studies Academy

Richard Delgrosso
Frick International Studies Academy

Janet Falkowski
Frick International Studies Academy

Joanne George
Reizenstein Middle School

Harriet Hopper
Reizenstein Middle School

Chuck Jessen
Reizenstein Middle School

Ken Labuskes
Reizenstein Middle School

Barbara Lewis
Reizenstein Middle School

Sharon Mihalich
Reizenstein Middle School

Marianne O'Connor
Frick International Studies Academy

Mark Sammartino
Reizenstein Middle School

Washington

Seattle

Chris Johnson
University Preparatory Academy

Rick Purn
University Preparatory Academy

Contents

Algebra is the centerpiece of most standard secondary school mathematics curricula. Traditionally, the goal of algebra instruction has been the development of students' proficiency in working with symbolic expressions. Students learn to use symbolic expressions to represent and reason about numerical situations and to solve equations and inequalities, and they learn how to manipulate symbolic expressions into equivalent forms.

Access to graphing calculators and computers has led to new goals for school algebra. The focus is shifting to functions and their use in modeling patterns of quantitative change, and greater emphasis is being placed on nonsymbolic representations such as graphs and tables. Instruction in routine symbol manipulation is often delayed until students have a firm understanding of the concepts required to support meaningful work with symbolic expressions.

The algebra strand in Connected Mathematics reflects this powerful new approach to algebraic instruction. Beginning in grade 6, students learn to examine multiple representations—equations, graphs, tables, diagrams, and verbal descriptions—to help them understand mathematical relationships. Throughout the curriculum, students are encouraged to use scientific and graphing calculators as tools for learning and problem solving. And, compared to more traditional curricula, less time is devoted to teaching procedures for manipulating symbolic expressions.

Of course, a basic understanding of and skill in the use of symbolic expressions are valuable mathematical tools. The concepts taught in *Say It with Symbols* convey the core knowledge of symbolic algebra that we feel is appropriate for students nearing the end of middle school mathematics.

Interpreting and writing symbolic expressions are central ideas in this unit. As students work to make sense of symbolic expressions and to evaluate expressions for specific values of the variables, they begin to focus on order of operations. They learn that different ways of reasoning about a situation can lead to different, yet equivalent, expressions. If two expressions both capture valid ways of thinking about a situation, students can conclude that the expressions are equivalent. Students can verify the equivalence of expressions by checking that the related graphs and tables are similar. Students also learn to use the distributive and commutative properties to transform expressions into equivalent forms. Finally, students apply their knowledge of equivalent expressions to solve linear equations and simple quadratic equations.

The combination of students' considerable background in working with symbolic expressions and a commitment to the instructional model that encourages students to investigate problems using a variety of strategies necessitates a significant departure from standard algebra teaching. Students' experiences with symbolic modeling of contextualized relationships can lead them naturally to conventions regarding order of operations, such as "multiplication before addition."

We want students to learn some basic ideas and skills of reasoning with purely symbolic expressions. However, we want those ideas and skills to make sense—to reflect what one does in *real* problem situations in which the symbolic expressions and manipulations have meaning. The problems presented to students in this unit will raise the necessary issues and provide a meaningful setting for introducing conventional algebraic notation and techniques.

Order of Operations

Throughout Connected Mathematics, students have encountered such problems as this: *The cost for N students to take a trip is C = 200 + 10N. How much will it cost for 15 students to take the trip?*

To answer this question, students must consider the order in which the mathematical operations must be performed. Do you add 200 and 10 and then multiply by 15? Or do you multiply 10 by 15 and then add 200? In this situation, students are evaluating an expression in a context that naturally guides the order of operations. By solving problems in meaningful contexts, students have already developed intuition about order of operations. In this unit, they will apply their intuitive understanding to evaluate expressions in purely mathematical contexts.

Equivalent Expressions

In *Thinking with Mathematical Models; Growing, Growing, Growing;* and *Frogs, Fleas, and Painted Cubes;* and in the grade 7 unit *Moving Straight Ahead,* students explored ways in which real and fictitious relationships can be expressed in tables, graphs, and equations. The contextual clues or the patterns in tables or graphs were usually so influential in the construction of the equation that only one version of the equation emerged. In *Say It with Symbols,* students are deliberately presented with situations in which contextual clues can be interpreted in several ways to produce different, yet equivalent, equations.

For example, in Problem 2.1, students are asked to find the number of 1-foot-square tiles needed to make a border around a square pool with sides of length *s* feet. Different conceptualizations of the situation can lead to these different, yet equivalent, equations for the number of tiles:

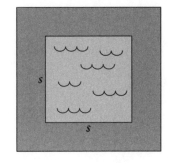

$N = 4s + 4$

$N = 4(s + 1)$

$N = s + s + s + s + 4$

$N = 8 + 4(s - 1)$

$N = 4(s + 2) - 4$

$N = 2s + 2(s + 2)$

$N = (s + 2)^2 - s^2$

1 ft

1 ft

border tile

To show that the expressions for area are equivalent, students may consider the reasonableness of the geometric reasoning represented by each equation, or they may check whether the equations have similar graphs and tables.

The Distributive Property

Although students can verify the equivalence of expressions by reasoning about the context or by comparing graphs and tables, it is important that they develop methods for showing equivalence by using symbolic reasoning.

The distributive property emerges naturally from Problem 2.3, in which students analyze swimming pools that are divided into sections. Students find various methods for computing the surface area of the water. For example, to find the area of the pool shown below, you can multiply the length of the entire pool by the width, $30(50 + 20)$, or you can add the areas of the two small sections, $30(50) + 30(20)$.

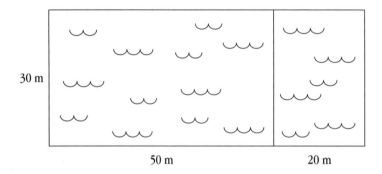

The equivalence of these two methods, $30(50 + 20) = 30(50) + 30(20)$, illustrates the distributive property. Specific examples lead students to the general case, as illustrated below.

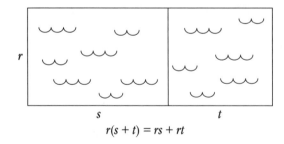

$$r(s + t) = rs + rt$$

If an expression is written as a factor multiplied by a sum, the distributive property can be applied to *multiply* the factor by each term in the sum. If an expression is written as a sum of terms and the terms have a common factor, the distributive property can be applied to rewrite the expression as the common factor multiplied by a sum, the process called *factoring*.

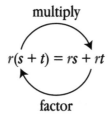

multiply

$$r(s + t) = rs + rt$$

factor

The distributive property allows students to group symbols or to expand an expression as needed. For example, suppose students are asked to find the total expenditure for a bike trip involving a food cost of $5 per person and a bike rental fee of $10 per person. Some students may reason that the cost of the trip is the cost for the food for all riders plus fees for the bikes for all riders, or $5n + 10n$. Others may reason that each rider must pay $15 for the bike trip, so the total cost is $15n$. The distributive property can be used to verify the equivalence of these expressions:

$$5n + 10n = (5 + 10)n = 15n$$

Realistic problems can also lead to the rule for distributing a negative sign. For example, suppose a checking account contains $100 at the start of the week. Two checks are written during the week, one for $22 and one for $50. Students may find the balance in the account at the end of the week in two ways:

$$100 - (22 + 50) = 28 \quad \text{or} \quad 100 - 22 - 50 = 28$$

Problems such as this suggest the general idea that $a - (b + c) = a - b - c$.

The Commutative Properties

Students are already familiar with the commutative properties from their experiences with arithmetic. In *Say It with Symbols*, these properties are revisited in an algebraic context. For example, the total area of the figure below can be expressed as $rs + rt$ or as $rt + rs$. The order in which the two areas are added does not matter.

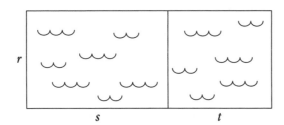

In this unit, students will eventually encounter symbolic statements of the commutative properties:

$$a + b = b + a \quad \text{and} \quad ab = ba$$

Some teachers prefer to refer to these properties as the *rearrangement properties* because this term has more meaning for students.

Solving Equations

In the grade 7 unit *Moving Straight Ahead*, students solved linear equations of the form $y = mx + b$. In this unit, they solve more complicated linear equations. To solve such equations, students use the strategy of *undoing* the mathematical operations until the variable is isolated on one side of the equation, being careful to apply mathematical operations to both sides.

In addition to solving linear equations, students also solve quadratic equations of the form $ax^2 + bx = 0$ and $(ax + b)(cx + d) = 0$. To solve $2x^2 + 8x = 0$, for example, students first need to recognize that $2x^2 + 8x$ can be rewritten in the equivalent form $2x(x + 4)$. They then must reason that this product can be zero only if one of the factors, $2x$ or $x + 4$, is equal to zero. If $2x = 0$ or $x + 4 = 0$, then $x = 0$ or $x = {}^-4$. In *Say It with Symbols*, students also learn that solving a quadratic equation of the form $ax^2 + bx + c = 0$ is equivalent to finding the x-intercepts of the graph of $y = ax^2 + bx + c$.

The Connected Mathematics Approach to Teaching Algebra Concepts

For teachers familiar with traditional algebra curriculum, the topics outlined above constitute a substantial portion of one year's work. However, it is important to keep in mind how the instruction of algebra in this program differs from that of more traditional programs.

First, the unit builds on several previous algebra units: *Variables and Patterns; Moving Straight Ahead; Thinking with Mathematical Models; Growing, Growing, Growing;* and *Frogs, Fleas, and Painted Cubes*. Students have been using symbolic expressions to represent and reason about variable quantities since early in the second year of the Connected Mathematics course. *Say It with Symbols* brings together and generalizes properties and operations with which students have already had extensive practice in more specific contexts.

Second, a conventional algebra course begins by enumerating a minimal set of real-number properties from which all other necessary manipulation procedures can be derived. Only then are the manipulations applied to expressions that model real problem situations. The Connected Mathematics approach takes a nearly opposite tack. Instead of trying to convince students that $x(x + 3) = x^2 + 3x$ for all values of x because multiplication distributes over addition, it conveys the idea that multiplication distributes over addition because in real-life or problem situations in which it makes sense to multiply x and $(x + 3)$, it turns out that the result is always equal to $x^2 + 3x$. That is, the intention is to build on students' experiences with symbolic expressions in contextualized problem settings to formulate the familiar algebraic "laws" of pure mathematics.

Third, *Say It with Symbols* continues to help students develop mathematical understanding through work on nontrivial problems. The important rules for working with symbolic expressions are embedded in contextual problems so that they can be approached using the same Launch-Explore-Summarize instructional model featured in the Connected Mathematics units. Thus, students will be challenged to sort out the meaning of symbolic expressions and operations and then asked to share their findings and ideas with the class in summary discussions.

Connected Mathematics was developed with the belief that calculators should always be available and that students should decide when to use them. Students will need access to graphing calculators for much of their work in this unit. Occasionally students will be asked not to use their calculators to encourage them to think about the order in which they must perform mathematical operations.

Mathematical and Problem-Solving Goals

Say It with Symbols **was created to help students**

- Review and strengthen their understanding of the conventional *order of operation* rules in the context of practical problems

- Evaluate expressions by applying the rules of order of operations

- Write symbolic sentences that communicate their reasoning

- Develop tools for manipulating symbolic expressions in ways that are both connected to and independent from tabular, graphical, and contextualized reasoning

- Recognize applications of the distributive and commutative properties

- Recognize and interpret equivalent expressions

- Reason about and with equivalent expressions

- Explain the reasoning underlying the solution of linear equations

- To make sense of symbolic expressions involving addition, subtraction, multiplication, division, and exponents

- To judge the equivalency of two or more expressions by examining the underlying reasoning and the related tables and graphs

- Apply the properties for manipulating expressions to solving linear equations

- Solve simple quadratic equations with some sense of basic factoring and "undoing" techniques

An overall goal of the Connected Mathematics curriculum is to help students to develop sound mathematical habits. Through their work in this and other algebra units, students learn important questions to ask themselves about any situation that can be represented and modeled mathematically, such as: *What rules govern the way expressions are evaluated? Is there more than one way to evaluate an expression? How can I tell if two expressions are equivalent? Which form of an expression should I use? What additional information is revealed by an equivalent form of an expression? What properties of real numbers are useful to help confirm that two or more expressions are equivalent? How can the distributive and commutative properties be applied to solve problems? What properties of real numbers are needed to solve linear and quadratic equations?*

Investigation 1: Order of Operations

Students continue, from their earlier work, to develop their intuition about the order in which operations in symbolic expressions should be performed. The problems highlight conventions of mathematical notation governing order of operations and evaluating expressions that involve addition, subtraction, multiplication, division, and exponents. Real-world contexts help students uncover and begin to apply these rules.

Investigation 2: Equivalent Expressions

Students have an opportunity to justify, in their own ways, the equivalence of two or more symbolic expressions for the same situation. They are encouraged to think about problems in a variety of ways, leading to different, yet equivalent, expressions. They also compare graphs and tables for equivalent expressions. In addition, the structures of the problems make it inevitable that important properties of numbers will be articulated and used, especially the distributive property. By the conclusion of the investigation, students will have developed a strong sense of the distributive property independent of a specific context.

Investigation 3: Some Important Properties

Students now acquire formal vocabulary for describing their prior experiences, learning the names of the distributive property and the commutative properties. This is a significant moment in students' development of algebraic skills. If students memorize such properties without understanding why they work, they will be able to apply the "patterns" to obvious examples, but will have no power to recognize the patterns in varied forms and situations. To achieve fluency with these skills, students talk about the ideas, devise their own examples, embed the properties in different contexts, and have an opportunity to uncover them in disguised situations. Throughout the investigation, students use the properties of real numbers to write equivalent expressions as they continue to connect symbolic expressions with real-world contexts. Both linear and quadratic expressions are explored.

Investigation 4: Solving Equations

Students review and extend their earlier work with linear equations, quadratic equations, and equivalent expressions, bringing together their experiences to establish systematic methods of solving equations. Students review how to solve a linear equation using a graph and a table, and they review the symbolic method for solving linear equations. They learn more about symbolic strategies for solving equations of the form $ax + b = cx + d$, and they are introduced to symbolic solutions for equations of the form $y = ax^2 + bx$. The ultimate goal is for students to become aware of the strengths and weaknesses of each solution method.

Investigation 5: Writing Expressions for Surface Area

Students are asked to find an expression for the surface area of a staggered stack of N rods of a particular length. The problem can be approached in several ways, and the various ways of reasoning will lead to different, but equivalent, expressions for modeling the data. Each expression will represent a pattern that a particular student or group saw in the data or will reflect the logic that was applied to the situation. Students can verify that the expressions are equivalent by using tables and graphs, by validating the underlying logic, and by applying the properties of real numbers. This activity provides a review of order of operations, writing and comparing equivalent expressions, and solving linear equations.

The ideas in *Say It with Symbols* build on and connect to several big ideas in other Connected Mathematics units.

Big Idea	Prior Work	Future Work
making sense of symbols	making sense of linear, quadratic, exponential, and other symbolic expressions *(Variables and Patterns; Moving Straight Ahead; Thinking with Mathematical Models; Growing, Growing, Growing; Frogs, Fleas, and Painted Cubes)*	making sense of polynomial, logarithmic, trigonometric, and rational symbolic expressions and functions *(high school)*
using the appropriate order of operations in evaluating expressions	evaluating and making sense of symbolic expressions *(Variables and Patterns; Moving Straight Ahead; Thinking with Mathematical Models; Growing, Growing, Growing; Frogs, Fleas, and Painted Cubes)*	evaluating and making sense of polynomial, logarithmic, trigonometric, and rational expressions *(high school)*
writing symbolic sentences, using parentheses and properties of real numbers, to communicate effectively	writing symbolic sentences *(Variables and Patterns; Moving Straight Ahead; Thinking with Mathematical Models; Growing, Growing, Growing; Frogs, Fleas, and Painted Cubes)*	writing equivalent expressions involving polynomial, logarithmic, trigonometric, and rational expressions that communicate reasoning using the properties of real numbers *(high school)*
reasoning with equivalent expressions	reasoning with equivalent expressions *(Bits and Pieces I; Bits and Pieces II; Variables and Patterns; Moving Straight Ahead; Thinking with Mathematical Models; Growing, Growing, Growing; Frogs, Fleas, and Painted Cubes)*	reasoning with equivalent expressions to solve problems that can be modeled by polynomial, logarithmic, trigonometric, and rational functions *(high school)*

Big Idea	Prior Work	Future Work
solving linear and quadratic equations	solving linear and quadratic equations using tables, graphs, and simple symbolic rules *(Variables and Patterns; Moving Straight Ahead; Thinking with Mathematical Models; Growing, Growing, Growing; Frogs, Fleas, and Painted Cubes)*	developing a deeper understanding of solving linear and quadratic equations and applying and extending the techniques to solving polynomial and rational equations *(high school)*
modeling and solving problems	modeling and solving problems *(Variables and Patterns; Moving Straight Ahead; Thinking with Mathematical Models; Growing, Growing, Growing; Frogs, Fleas, and Painted Cubes)*	modeling and solving problems using polynomial, logarithmic, and trigonometric functions *(high school)*

Materials

For students

- Labsheet UP (optional; 1 per student)
- Trapezoids cut from Labsheet 3.3 (optional)
- Graphing calculators (preferably with the capacity to display a function as a table)
- Square tiles (optional)
- Cuisenaire® rods (4 to 6 of the same color rod plus 3 or 4 unit rods per pair of students)
- Manufactured cubes or sugar cubes (optional, for the Unit Project; ideally at least 60 per student)
- Grid paper (provided as a blackline master)
- Isometric dot paper (optional, for the Unit Project; provided as a blackline master)
- Transparent grids (optional; copy the grid onto transparency film)
- Centimeter rulers (optional)
- Large sheets of paper (at least 1 per pair)
- Blank transparencies (optional)

For the teacher

- Transparencies and transparency markers (optional)
- Transparency of Labsheet 3.3 (optional)
- Transparent grid (optional; copy the grid onto transparency film)
- Overhead display model of students' graphing calculators (optional)
- Pan balance (optional)
- Square tiles for the overhead (optional)
- Cuisenaire rods for the overhead (optional)

Resources

Books

Heid, Kathleen. *Algebra in a Technological World: NCTM Addenda Series Grades 9–12*. Reston, Va.: National Council of Teachers of Mathematics, 1995.

Winter, Mary Jean, and Ronald J. Carlson. *Algebra Experiments I: Exploring Linear Functions*. Menlo Park, Calif.: Addison-Wesley, 1993.

Software

Dugale, Sharon, and David Kibbey. *Green Globs and Graphing Equations* (IBM, Apple II, Macintosh). Pleasantville, N.Y.: Sunburst Communications.

Rosenberg, Jon. *Math Connections: Algebra I* (Macintosh). Pleasantville, N.Y.: Sunburst Communications.

Pacing Chart

This pacing chart gives estimates of the class time required for each investigation and assessment piece. Shaded rows indicate opportunities for assessment.

Investigations and Assessments	Class Time
1 Order of Operations	4 days
Check-Up 1	$\frac{1}{2}$ day
2 Equivalent Expressions	4 days
3 Some Important Properties	5 days
Quiz	1 day
4 Solving Equations	5 days
Check-Up 2	$\frac{1}{2}$ day
5 Writing Expressions for Surface Area	2 days
Self-Assessment	Take home
Final Assessment (Unit Test or Unit Project)	1 or 2 days

Say It with Symbols Vocabulary

The following words and concepts are used in *Say It with Symbols*. Concepts in the left column are those essential for student understanding of this and future units. The Descriptive Glossary gives descriptions of many of these terms.

Essential terms developed in this unit
commutative property
  of addition
commutative property
  of multiplication
distributive property
equivalent expressions
expanded form
factored form
parabola
roots
term

Terms developed in previous units
algebraic expression
function
linear relationship
quadratic relationship
surface area
x-intercept
y-intercept

Nonessential term
order of operations

Embedded Assessment

Opportunities for informal assessment of student progress are embedded throughout *Say It with Symbols* in the problems, the ACE questions, and the Mathematical Reflections. Suggestions for observing as students explore and discover mathematical ideas, for probing to guide their progress in developing concepts and skills, and for questioning to determine their level of understanding can be found in the Launch, Explore, and Summarize sections of all investigation problems. Some examples:

- Investigation 4, Problem 4.4 *Launch* (page 64i) suggests a way to help students discover for themselves the mathematical reasoning underlying the process of solving a quadratic equation by first factoring it.
- Investigation 1, Problem 1.1 *Explore* (page 19a) suggests questions to help assess and help strengthen students' intuitive understanding of order of operations.
- Investigation 3, Problem 3.1 *Summarize* (page 52c) suggests a quick class activity that can be used at various points in the unit to assess students' current understanding of algebraic expressions, and to help them learn to apply the principles of algebra independent of a specific context.

ACE Assignments

An ACE (Applications—Connections—Extensions) section appears at the end of each investigation. To help you assign ACE questions, a list of assignment choices is given in the margin next to the reduced student page for each problem. Each list indicates the ACE questions that students should be able to answer after they complete the problem.

Check-Ups

Two check-ups, which may be given after Investigations 1 and 4, are provided for use as quick quizzes or warm-up activities. The check-ups are designed for students to complete individually. You will find the check-ups and their answer keys in the Assessment Resources section.

Partner Quiz

One quiz, which may be given after Investigation 3, is provided with this unit. The quiz is designed to be completed by pairs of students with the opportunity for revision based on teacher feedback. You will find the quiz and its answer key in the Assessment Resources section. As an alternative to the quiz provided, you can construct your own quiz by combining questions from the Question Bank, this quiz, and unassigned ACE questions.

Question Bank

A Question Bank provides questions you can use for homework, reviews, or quizzes. You will find the Question Bank and its answer key in the Assessment Resources section.

Notebook/Journal

Students should have notebooks to record and organize their work. Notebooks should include student journals and sections for vocabulary, homework, quizzes, and check-ups. In their journals, students can take notes, solve investigation problems, and record their ideas about Mathematical Reflections questions. Journals should be assessed for completeness rather than correctness; they should be seen as "safe" places where students can try out their thinking. A Notebook Checklist and a Self-Assessment are provided in the Assessment Resources section. The Notebook Checklist helps students organize their notebooks. The Self-Assessment guides students as they review their notebooks to determine which ideas they have mastered and which they still need to work on.

The Unit Test

The final assessment in *Say It with Symbols* is either the unit test or the unit project. The unit test focuses on identifying and writing equivalent expressions; evaluating expressions; solving linear and quadratic equations; and relating tabular, graphic, and symbolic forms of representing relationships.

The Unit Project

The final assessment in *Say It with Symbols* is either the unit test or the unit project. The hands-on unit project offers students an opportunity to apply what they have learned about observing patterns, writing algebraic expressions to describe those patterns, and verifying the equivalence of different expressions that represent the same pattern.

Introducing Your Students to *Say It with Symbols*

This introduction will raise issues related to reading, interpreting, and evaluating symbolic expressions and to finding equivalent expressions. To begin the unit, remind students of some of the symbolic expressions that they have investigated in previous units, such as the grade 7 units *Variables and Patterns* and *Moving Straight Ahead* and the grade 8 units *Growing, Growing, Growing* and *Frogs, Fleas, and Painted Cubes*.

Ask the class to give some of the symbolic expressions that were used to represent linear, quadratic, and exponential relationships in the problems they investigated in earlier units, or make up an example of each. You might want to have some students discuss what information the symbols represent in the problems and how they can use these expressions to find the values of the variables.

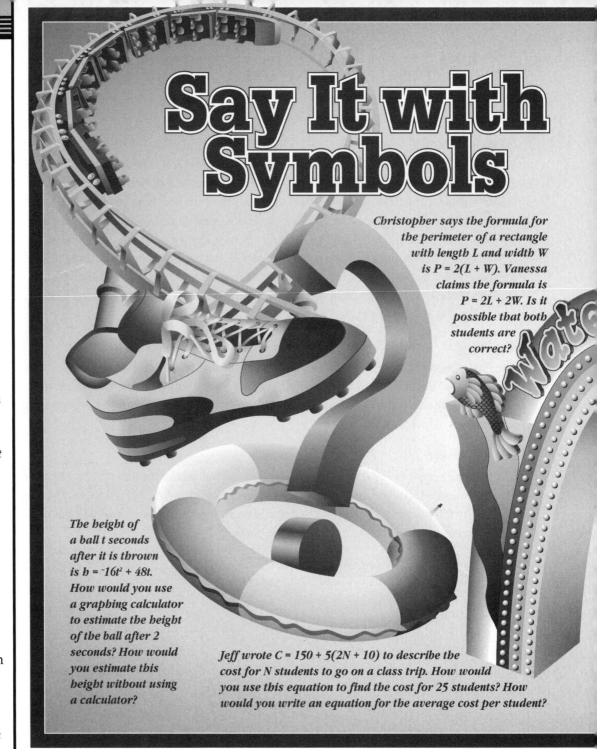

Say It with Symbols

Christopher says the formula for the perimeter of a rectangle with length L and width W is $P = 2(L + W)$. Vanessa claims the formula is $P = 2L + 2W$. Is it possible that both students are correct?

The height of a ball t seconds after it is thrown is $b = {}^-16t^2 + 48t$. How would you use a graphing calculator to estimate the height of the ball after 2 seconds? How would you estimate this height without using a calculator?

Jeff wrote $C = 150 + 5(2N + 10)$ to describe the cost for N students to go on a class trip. How would you use this equation to find the cost for 25 students? How would you write an equation for the average cost per student?

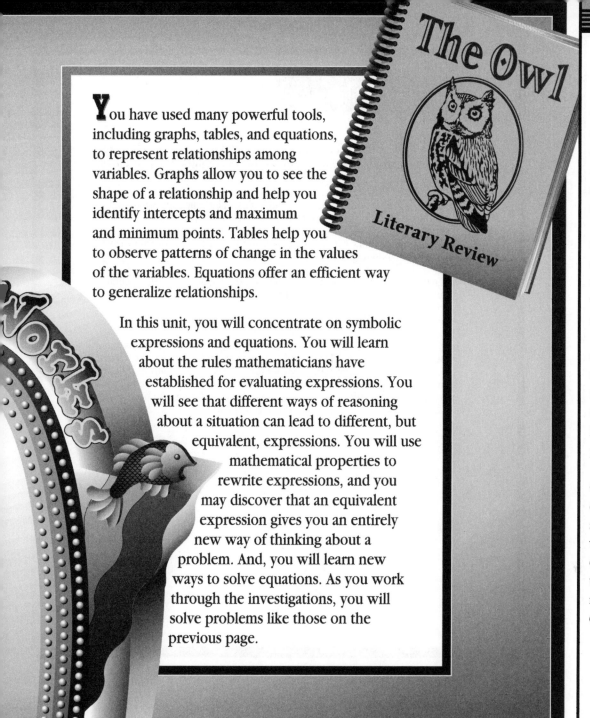

You have used many powerful tools, including graphs, tables, and equations, to represent relationships among variables. Graphs allow you to see the shape of a relationship and help you identify intercepts and maximum and minimum points. Tables help you to observe patterns of change in the values of the variables. Equations offer an efficient way to generalize relationships.

In this unit, you will concentrate on symbolic expressions and equations. You will learn about the rules mathematicians have established for evaluating expressions. You will see that different ways of reasoning about a situation can lead to different, but equivalent, expressions. You will use mathematical properties to rewrite expressions, and you may discover that an equivalent expression gives you an entirely new way of thinking about a problem. And, you will learn new ways to solve equations. As you work through the investigations, you will solve problems like those on the previous page.

Spend a few minutes with the class discussing the three examples and the related questions in the student edition. Listen as students share their ideas about each example.

Can they evaluate the motion equation for a given value of the independent variable? In what order do they suggest doing the operations?

Can they explain how Christopher and Vanessa are thinking about the rectangle? Can they write another formula to express the perimeter?

Can they evaluate the cost equation for a given value and describe the order in which they performed the operations? What ideas do they have about what it means to find an "average" cost?

Mathematical Highlights

The Mathematical Highlights page was designed to provide information to students and to parents and other family members. This page gives students a preview of the activities and problems in *Say It with Symbols*. As they work through the unit, students can refer back to the Mathematical Highlights page to review what they have learned and to preview what is still to come. This page also tells parents and other family members what mathematical ideas and activities will be covered as the class works through *Say It with Symbols*.

Mathematical Highlights

In *Say It With Symbols* you will extend your ability to use symbolic expressions to describe and reason about relations between variables. The unit should help you to

● Use *order of operations* rules to write and evaluate algebraic expressions and equations that model quantitative patterns and relationships;

● Interpret given symbolic expressions to discover the relations between variables that are implied by those expressions;

● Understand and apply properties of numbers and operations to write algebraic expressions and equations in equivalent forms; and

● Solve linear and quadratic equations by symbolic reasoning.

As you work on the problems of this unit, make it a habit to ask questions about problem situations that involve symbolic expressions and equations: *What symbolic expression or equation correctly expresses the sequence of calculations required by given conditions? Is there a way that a given expression or equation can be written in equivalent form to provide new information about a relationship? What operations would transform a given equation into an equivalent form from which the solution will be clear?*

The Investigations

The teaching materials for each investigation consist of three parts: an overview, student pages with teaching outlines, and detailed notes for teaching the investigation.

The overview of each investigation includes brief descriptions of the problems, the mathematical and problem-solving goals of the investigation, and a list of necessary materials.

Essential information for teaching the investigation is provided in the margins around the student pages. The "At a Glance" overviews are brief outlines of the Launch, Explore, and Summarize phases of each problem for reference as you work with the class. To help you assign homework, a list of "Assignment Choices" is provided next to each problem. Where space permits, answers to problems, follow-ups, ACE questions, and Mathematical Reflections appear next to the appropriate student pages.

The Teaching the Investigation section follows the student pages and is the heart of the Connected Mathematics curriculum. This section describes in detail the Launch, Explore, and Summarize phases for each problem. It includes all the information needed for teaching, along with suggestions for what you might say at key points in the teaching. Use this section to prepare lessons and as a guide for teaching the investigations.

Assessment Resources

The Assessment Resources section contains blackline masters and answer keys for the check-ups, the quiz, the Question Bank, and the Unit Test. Blackline masters for the Notebook Checklist and the Self-Assessment are given. These instruments support student self-evaluation, an important aspect of assessment in the Connected Mathematics curriculum. A discussion of how one teacher assessed Check-Up 1 is included, along with a suggested scoring rubric and samples of student work. This section also includes a guide to the Unit Project.

Blackline Masters

The Blackline Masters section includes masters for all labsheets and transparencies. Blackline masters of grid paper and isometric dot paper are also provided.

Additional Practice

Practice pages for each investigation offer additional problems for students who need more prac-tice with the basic concepts developed in the investigations as well as some continual review of earlier concepts.

Descriptive Glossary

The glossary provides descriptions and examples of the key concepts in *Say It with Symbols*. These descriptions are not intended to be formal definitions but are meant to give you an idea of how students might make sense of these important concepts.

Order of Operations

This investigation will help students to develop their intuition about the order in which operations in symbolic expressions should be performed. The problems bring the issue of mathematical conventions governing order of operations to light as students evaluate expressions that involve addition, subtraction, multiplication, division, and exponents. Real-world contexts help students uncover and begin to apply these rules.

In Problem 1.1, Adding and Multiplying, students work with equations involving addition, subtraction, and multiplication. In the context of analyzing a business, they first apply the equation for specific values of the variables and then observe the order of operations that they used. In Problem 1.2, Dividing, students work with equations involving division. The realistic context helps them to make sense of expressions that represent division in a variety of forms, including fractions. Again, students are asked to observe the order in which they perform operations. Problem 1.3, Working with Exponents, reintroduces quadratic expressions and equations. Students work with expressions and equations involving exponents as well as with addition, subtraction, and multiplication and are again asked to discuss what order of operations seems appropriate.

Mathematical and Problem-Solving Goals

- **To make sense of symbolic expressions involving addition, subtraction, multiplication, division, and exponents**

- **To develop an understanding of the conventional order of operations rules by being attentive to the ways expressions are written and evaluated in a variety of settings**

- **To evaluate expressions by applying the rules of order of operations**

	Materials	
Problem	**For students**	**For the teacher**
All	Graphing calculators	Transparencies: 1.1 to 1.3B (optional), overhead graphing calculator (optional)

Order of Operations

Equations are an efficient way to communicate information about relationships among variables. To help us communicate clearly, mathematicians have established rules for writing and interpreting algebraic expressions. In this investigation, you will explore these rules.

Think about this!

The rugby club wants to order new jerseys. The jersey manufacturer tells the club members that they can figure out the total cost by using the equation

$$C = 100 + 15N$$

where C is the cost in dollars and N is the number of jerseys ordered. The team wants 20 jerseys. Pedro and David both calculate the amount the club will owe.

Pedro's calculation	David's calculation
$C = 100 + 15 \times 20$	$C = 100 + 15 \times 20$
$= 100 + 300$	$= 115 \times 20$
$= 400$	$= 2300$

Who did the calculation correctly? What mistake did the other boy make?

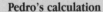

1.1 Adding and Multiplying

The Water Works amusement park features exciting water rides and slides. The park discounts admission prices for large groups. Group prices are determined by using the equation $p = 100 + 10a + 8c$, where p is the price in dollars, a is the number of adults, and c is the number of children.

- - - - - - - - - - - -
At a Glance

Grouping:
small groups

Launch

- Introduce the equation used by the amusement park to determine group admission prices.

- Have groups of three or four work on the problem.

Explore

- Ask each student to make a table.

- Ask questions to help students who are not performing operations in the correct order.

Summarize

- Have groups share their answers and resolve any differences.

- Talk about the meaning of the numbers in the equation.

- Assign and then review the follow-up.

Assignment Choices

ACE questions 1–5, 18–22, 29, and 31–33

Problem 1.1

As part of an advertising brochure, the Water Works marketing manager wants to include a table showing admission prices for groups with certain numbers of adults and children.

Group Admission Prices

		Number of children				
		20	40	60	80	100
Number of adults	10					
	20					
	30					
	40					

A. Copy and complete the table to show admission prices for groups with various numbers of adults and children. Do your calculations without using a calculator.

B. Look for patterns in the rows and columns of the table. Describe each pattern you find, and tell which part of the equation creates the pattern.

C. In the equation $p = 100 + 10a + 8c$, what do the numbers 100, 10, and 8 tell you about calculating the group price?

D. What mathematical operations do you need to perform to calculate the group price for a particular number of adults and children? In what order must you perform the operations?

Answers to Problem 1.1

A. See page 19h.

B. In each column, as the number of adults increases by 10, the group price increases by 100; the 10 in the equation creates this pattern (10 × 10 = 100). In each row, as the number of children increases by 20, the group price increases by 160; the 8 in the equation creates this pattern (20 × 8 = 160).

C. 100 represents the basic group price of $100, 10 is the cost of an adult's ticket in dollars, and 8 is the cost of a child's ticket in dollars.

D. The operations are multiplication and addition. Multiply the price of an adult's ticket by the number of adults, multiply the price of a child's ticket by the number of children, and then add these two products to 100.

■ **Problem 1.1 Follow-Up**

The Water Works business manager used data collected over the past several years to write equations that help him make predictions about the daily operations of the park.

1. The daily profit in dollars, P, from the park concession stands depends on the number of visitors, V. The business manager wrote the equation $P = 2.50V - 500$ to model this relationship.

   a. If 300 people visit the park, about how much concession profit will be made? Do your calculations without using a calculator.

   b. If 600 people visit the park, about how much concession profit will be made? Do your calculations without using a calculator.

   c. What mathematical operations did you perform to calculate your answers in parts a and b? In what order did you perform the operations?

   d. Check your answer from part a by entering $2.5 \times 300 - 500$ on a graphing calculator and pressing [ENTER]. Check your answer for part b by entering $2.5 \times 600 - 500$ and pressing [ENTER]. Do the results agree with the results you found by doing the calculations by hand?

2. The manager uses the equation $V = 600 - 500R$ to predict the number of visitors based on the probability of rain, R.

   a. If the probability of rain is 25%, about how many people will visit the park? Do your calculations without using a calculator.

   b. If the probability of rain is 75%, about how many people will visit the park? Do your calculations without using a calculator.

   c. What mathematical operations did you perform to calculate your answers in parts a and b? In what order did you perform the operations?

   d. Use a graphing calculator to check your answers from parts a and b. Do the results agree with the results you found by doing the calculations by hand?

Investigation 1: Order of Operations 7

Answers to Problem 1.1 Follow-Up

1. a. $P = 2.50(300) - 500 = 750 - 500 = \$250$

   b. $P = 2.50(600) - 500 = 1500 - 500 = \$1000$

   c. The operations are multiplication and subtraction. Multiplication is done before subtraction.

   d. The answers agree.

2. a. $V = 600 - 500(0.25) = 600 - 125 = 475$ visitors

   b. $V = 600 - 500(0.75) = 600 - 375 = 225$ visitors

   c. The operations are multiplication and subtraction. Multiplication is done before subtraction.

   d. The answers agree.

Investigation 1 7

Launch

- Develop the equation for the average per-visitor concession profit.

- Have groups of three or four work on the problem.

Explore

- Ask each student to make a table.

- Ask questions to help students who are not performing operations in the correct sequence.

Summarize

- Discuss each part of the problem.

- Assign and then review the follow-up.

- Summarize what students have discovered about the order in which operations should be performed.

3. Use the equations from questions 1 and 2 to answer these questions.
   a. If the probability of rain is 50%, about how much profit will be made from the concession stands?
   b. If the probability of rain is 10%, about how much profit will be made from the concession stands?
   c. What mathematical operations did you perform to calculate your answers in parts a and b? In what order did you perform the operations?

4. You can combine the equations from questions 1 and 2 into a single equation. Since $V = 600 - 500R$, you can substitute the expression $600 - 500R$ for V in the equation $P = 2.50V - 500$. This gives the equation $P = 2.50(600 - 500R) - 500$, which tells you the expected concession profit in terms of the probability of rain. The parentheses indicate that you should evaluate $600 - 500R$ *before* multiplying by 2.50.
   a. Use this equation to find the expected concession profit if the probability of rain is 50% and if the probability of rain is 10%. Check both results with your calculator.
   b. How do your answers compare with the results you found in parts a and b of question 3?

5. The equations used by the Water Works business manager involve addition, subtraction, and multiplication. When you evaluate expressions with these operations, in what order should you perform the operations? For example, what steps would you follow to evaluate $40 - 5x + 7y$ when $x = 3$ and $y = 5$?

1.2 Dividing

As with division of numbers, division of algebraic expressions is often shown as a fraction. In the last problem, you saw that the daily concession profit at Water Works can be predicted by the equation $P = 2.50V - 500$. The business manager used this profit equation to derive the following equation for the average daily concession profit per visitor:

$$A = \frac{2.50V - 500}{V}$$

Assignment Choices

ACE questions 23–28, 30, and unassigned choices from earlier problems

3. a. $V = 600 - 500(0.50) = 600 - 250 = 350$, so $P = 2.50(350) - 500 = 875 - 500 = \$375$

   b. $V = 600 - 500(0.10) = 600 - 50 = 550$, so $P = 2.50(550) - 500 = 1375 - 500 = \$875$

   c. The operations are multiplication and subtraction. In each step, multiplication is done before subtraction.

4. a. $P = 2.50[600 - 500(0.50)] - 500 = \$375$, $P = 2.50[600 - 500(0.10)] - 500 = \$875$

   b. The answers are the same.

5. Multiplication should be done before addition or subtraction. To evaluate $40 - 5x + 7y$ for $x = 3$ and $y = 5$, multiply 5 by 3 and 7 by 5 and then perform the addition and subtraction: $40 - 5(3) + 7(5) = 40 - 15 + 35 = 60$.

Problem 1.2

A. 1. If 300 people visit the park, about how much concession profit will be made?

2. About how much concession profit will be made per visitor?

B. Copy and complete the table below to show the average per-visitor concession profit for various numbers of visitors. Do your calculations without using your calculator.

Visitors	100	200	300	400	500	600	700	800
Average profit								

C. Find the average per-visitor concession profit for 250, 350, and 425 visitors.

D. What mathematical operations do you need to perform to calculate the average per-visitor profit for a given number of visitors? In what order must you perform the operations?

E. The Water Works business manager claims that the average concession profit per visitor can also be calculated with either of these equations:

$$A = \frac{1}{V}(2.50V - 500) \qquad A = (2.50V - 500) \div V$$

Do you agree? Explain.

■ Problem 1.2 Follow-Up

1. a. Use the example of calculating the average per-visitor concession profit as a guide to help you evaluate $\frac{100 + 3x}{x}$ when $x = 25$.

b. Check your answer by entering an expression into your graphing calculator and pressing ENTER. What expression did you enter?

2. a. Use the example of calculating the average per-visitor concession profit as a guide to help you evaluate $\frac{3x}{4x + 3}$ when $x = 10$.

b. Check your answer by entering an expression into your graphing calculator and pressing ENTER. What expression did you enter?

3. When evaluating an expression that is in fraction form, in what order should you perform the operations?

Answers to Problem 1.2

A. 1. $P = 2.50(300) - 500 = 750 - 500 = \$250$ **2.** $\$250 \div 300 \approx \$0.83$ per visitor

B.

Visitors	100	200	300	400	500	600	700	800
Average profit	⁻$2.50	$0	$0.83	$1.25	$1.50	$1.67	$1.79	$1.88

C. $V = 250$: $A = \frac{2.50(250) - 500}{250} = \frac{625 - 500}{250} = \frac{125}{250} = \$0.50$

$V = 350$: $A = \frac{2.50(350) - 500}{350} = \frac{875 - 500}{350} = \frac{375}{350} \approx \$1.07$

$V = 425$: $A = \frac{2.50(425) - 500}{425} = \frac{1062.5 - 500}{425} = \frac{562.5}{425} \approx \$1.32$

D, E. See page 19h.

Answers to Problem 1.2 Follow-Up

See page 19h.

Working with Exponents

The president of Water Works wants a large arch built at the entrance to the park. He gave the architect the sketch and equation below. The equation gives the height, y, of the arch above a point x feet from one of the bases of the arch. This means that if you are standing under the arch x feet from one base, the point of the arch directly over your head will be $5x - 0.1x^2$ feet above the ground.

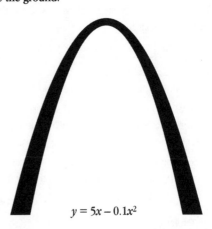

$$y = 5x - 0.1x^2$$

Problem 1.3

A. Use the equation to find the height of the arch at these distances from the left base. Do your calculations without using a calculator.
  1. 10 feet
  2. 30 feet
  3. 50 feet

B. What operations did you perform to calculate your answers for part A? In what order did you perform these operations?

C. Check your answers for part A by using a graphing calculator to help you make a table.

D. 1. The expression $5x - 0.1x^2$ is equivalent to the expression $0.1x(50 - x)$. Use this second expression to calculate the heights for the x values given in part A.

  2. In what order did you perform the operations?

At a Glance

Grouping:
small groups

Launch

- As a class, discuss the equation for the arch.

- Have groups of three or four explore the problem and follow-up.

Explore

- Circulate as groups work, listening to their generalizations about the order of operations for expressions containing exponents.

Summarize

- Have students share their conclusions about expressions involving exponents.

- Talk about how such expressions are evaluated on a calculator.

- Use the arch equation to review quadratic relationships.

Assignment Choices

ACE questions 6–17, 34–42, and unassigned choices from earlier problems

Assessment

It is appropriate to use Check-Up 1 after this problem.

Answers to Problem 1.3

A. 1. $5(10) - 0.1(10^2) = 50 - 10 = 40$ ft   2. $5(30) - 0.1(30^2) = 150 - 90 = 60$ ft

    3. $5(50) - 0.1(50^2) = 250 - 250 = 0$ ft (Note: This is the location of the second base.)

B. Exponentiation, multiplication, and subtraction: raise the number to the exponent, multiply each pair of numbers to be multiplied, and then subtract the second product from the first. (Note: Multiplication of the term $5x$ could be performed first. Students may express the concept of exponentiation using different language.)

C.

Distance from one base (ft)	10	20	30	40	50
Height of arch (ft)	40	60	60	40	0

D. 1. $x = 10$: $0.1(10)(50 - 10) = 0.1(10)(40) = 40$ ft $x = 30$: $0.1(30)(50 - 30) = 0.1(30)(20) = 60$ ft

    $x = 50$: $0.1(50)(50 - 50) = 0.1(50)(0) = 0$ ft

■ **Problem 1.3 Follow-Up**

When a giant roller coaster was built at Water Works, attendance began to increase. The business manager wrote the equation $V = 1000(1.2^m)$ to estimate the daily number of visitors m months after the roller-coaster ride opened.

1. **a.** Estimate the number of visitors 1 month after the roller-coaster ride opened.
   b. Estimate the number of visitors 5 months after the roller-coaster ride opened.
   c. Estimate the number of visitors 12 months after the roller-coaster ride opened.

2. What operations did you perform to find your answers in question 1? In what order did you perform the operations?

3. Check your answer to part c of question 1 by entering an expression into your calculator and pressing ENTER. What expression did you enter?

Did you know?

Americans have been splashing at water-slide parks for more than 100 years! The first water park was opened in 1894 in Chicago's South Side by Captain Paul Boynton. The popular and successful "Captain Boynton's Water Chutes" was the first modernized amusement park in the world. The parked served as a model for amusement parks built during the recreation boom of the early 1900s.

D. 2. Perform the subtraction within the parentheses, and then multiply the three numbers. (Note: In a later investigation, students will find that they can distribute the $0.5x$ over the difference of the terms.)

Answers to Problem 1.3 Follow-Up

1. a. $V = 1000(1.2^1) = 1000(1.2) = 1200$ visitors
   b. $V = 1000(1.2^5) \approx 1000(2.488) = 2488$ visitors
   c. $V = 1000(1.2^{12}) \approx 1000(8.916) = 8916$ visitors

2. Exponentiation is done first, followed by multiplication.

3. Possible answer: $1000 \times 1.2 \wedge 12$

Applications

In 1–5, multiplication is done before addition or subtraction.

1. $3(12) + 15 = 51$
2. $25 + 8(2) = 41$
3. $10(4) - 12 = 28$
4. $-3(7) + 10 = -11$
5. $40 - 5(6) = 10$

In 6–9, exponentiation is done before multiplication.

6. $5(4^2) = 80$
7. $5(-3)^2 = 45$
8. $-3(4^2) = -48$
9. $-3(-4)^2 = -48$

In 10–12, exponentiation is done first, then multiplication, and then addition and/or subtraction.

10. $4(7^2) + 3(7) = 217$
11. $4(-7)^2 + 3(-7) = 175$
12. $4(7^2) - 3(7) = 175$

As you work on these ACE questions, use your calculator whenever you need it.

Applications

In 1–5, evaluate the expression for the given x value, and describe the order in which you performed the operations.

1. $3x + 15$ when $x = 12$
2. $25 + 8x$ when $x = 2$
3. $10x - 12$ when $x = 4$
4. $-3x + 10$ when $x = 7$
5. $40 - 5x$ when $x = 6$

In 6–9, evaluate the expression for the given x value, and describe the order in which you performed the operations.

6. $5x^2$ when $x = 4$
7. $5x^2$ when $x = -3$
8. $-3x^2$ when $x = 4$
9. $-3x^2$ when $x = -4$

In 10–17, evaluate the expression for the given x value, and describe the order in which you performed the operations.

10. $4x^2 + 3x$ when $x = 7$
11. $4x^2 + 3x$ when $x = -7$
12. $4x^2 - 3x$ when $x = 7$

13. $4x^2 - 3x$ when $x = {}^-7$

14. $4x^2 + 3x + 5$ when $x = 2$

15. $4x^2 + 3x - 5$ when $x = 2$

16. $4x^2 - 3x - 5$ when $x = {}^-3$

17. $^-4x^2 - 3x - 5$ when $x = {}^-3$

In 18–22, evaluate the expression for the given x value, and describe the order in which you performed the operations.

18. $7(x + 8)$ when $x = {}^-3$

19. $7(5x + 8)$ when $x = 3$

20. $7(8 - 5x)$ when $x = 3$

21. $(8 - 5x)(3x + 2)$ when $x = 4$

22. $(x - 5)(x + 2)$ when $x = 10$

In 23–27, evaluate the expression for the given x value, and describe the order in which you performed the operations.

23. $\frac{36}{2x}$ when $x = 6$

24. $\frac{3x + 2}{5}$ when $x = 11$

25. $\frac{72}{2x + 1}$ when $x = 4$

26. $\frac{50x + 10}{x}$ when $x = 2$

27. $\frac{8 + 3x}{x + 1}$ when $x = 4$

Investigation 1: Order of Operations　**13**

Teaching Tip: The class discussion of these problems is a good time to review the notion of symbols of inclusion. Parentheses and brackets are used to tell which operation to do first. The operation indicated by the innermost symbols of inclusion is performed first.

In 13–17, exponentiation is done first, then multiplication, and then addition and/or subtraction.

13. $4({}^-7)^2 - 3({}^-7) = 217$

14. $4(2^2) + 3(2) + 5 = 27$

15. $4(2^2) + 3(2) - 5 = 17$

16. $4({}^-3)^2 - 3({}^-3) - 5 = 40$

17. $^-4({}^-3)^2 - 3({}^-3) - 5 = {}^-32$

18. $7({}^-3 + 8) = 35$; Addition is done before multiplication.

19. $7[5(3) + 8] = 161$; Multiplication and then addition are done inside the parentheses, and then multiplication.

20. $7[8 - 5(3)] = {}^-49$; Multiplication and then subtraction are done inside the parentheses, and then multiplication.

21. $[8 - 5(4)][3(4) + 2] = {}^-168$; Multiplication and then subtraction and addition are done inside the parentheses, and then multiplication.

22. $(10 - 5)(10 + 2) = 60$; subtraction and addition, multiplication

23. $\frac{36}{2(6)} = 3$; multiplication, division

In 24–27, multiplication is performed first, then addition, and then division.

24. $\frac{3(11) + 2}{5} = 7$

25. $\frac{72}{2(4) + 1} = 8$

26. $\frac{50(2) + 10}{2} = 55$

27. $\frac{8 + 3(4)}{4 + 1} = 4$

28a. $2 + 3(4) \div 2 = 8$

28b. Possible answers: $2 + \frac{3x}{2}, 2 + \frac{3}{2}x$

28c. $2 + \frac{3(4)}{2} = 8$; The answers are the same.

Connections

29a. Gish's estimate is correct: $C = 200 + 10(50) = 200 + 500 = \$700$.

29b. Duncan performed the operations incorrectly by doing the addition first: $C = (200 + 10)50 = \$10,500$.

30a. $S = \frac{200 + 10(N)}{N}$

30b. $S = \frac{200 + 10(20)}{20} = \frac{200 + 200}{20} = \frac{400}{20} = \$20$

30c. $S = \frac{200 + 10(40)}{40} = \frac{200 + 400}{40} = \frac{600}{40} = \$15$

---

28. **a.** Find the value of $2 + 3x \div 2$ when $x = 4$.

 b. Write an expression that is equivalent to $2 + 3x \div 2$ and that includes a fraction.

 c. Evaluate the expression you wrote in part b for $x = 4$. How does your result compare to the result you found in part a?

Connections

In 29 and 30, use this information: The ski club is planning a trip for winter break. They wrote the equation $C = 200 + 10N$ to estimate the cost in dollars of the trip if N students attend.

29. Duncan and Gish both used the equation to estimate the cost for 50 students. Duncan said the cost would be \$10,500, and Gish said it would be \$700.

 a. Determine which estimate is correct. Show the calculations needed to find the estimate.

 b. How do you think Duncan and Gish found such different estimates if they both used the same equation?

30. **a.** Write an equation for the cost per student, S, if N students go on the trip.

 b. What will be the cost per student if 20 students go on the trip?

 c. What will be the cost per student if 40 students go on the trip?

In 31–33, you will explore some relationships involved in the operation of Water Works.

31. The concession profit, in dollars, for *V* visitors can be estimated by the equation $P = 2.50V - 500$.

    a. Make a table of data for five *V* values.

    b. Graph the equation.

    c. Identify the slope and the *y*-intercept of the graph. Explain what each of these values tells you about the relationship between the variables.

32. The number of visitors can be estimated from the probability of rain, *R*, by using the equation $V = 600 - 500R$.

    a. Make a table of data for five *R* values.

    b. Graph the equation.

    c. Identify the slope and the *y*-intercept of the graph. Explain what each of these values tells you about the relationship between the variables.

33. The daily increase in the employee-bonus fund, in dollars, can be estimated from the number of visitors by using the equation $B = 100 + 0.50V$.

    a. Make a table of data for five *V* values.

    b. Graph the equation.

    c. Identify the slope and the *y*-intercept of the graph. Explain what each of these values tells you about the relationship between the variables.

In 34–39, you will practice evaluating familiar geometric formulas. As you evaluate each formula, think carefully about the order of operations.

34. The formula for the area of a circle with radius *r* is $A = \pi r^2$. Find the area of a circle with a radius of 4 centimeters.

31a. Possible table:

V	P
100	−250
200	0
300	250
400	500
500	750

31b. See below left.

31c. The slope is 2.5; it shows that for each additional visitor, profit increases by $2.50. The *y*-intercept is −500; it indicates a loss of $500 for days when no one visits the park. (**Teaching Tip:** Ask students what part of the graph makes sense in this situation; they should realize that negative values of *V* do not make sense. Also ask them what negative values of *P* represent; they indicate a loss of money for the park.)

32. See page 19i.

33. See page 19i.

34. $A = \pi(4^2) = \pi(16) \approx 50.27$ cm^2

31b.

Concession Profit

Profit (dollars) vs *Visitors*

35. $A = 6(5^2) = 6(25) =$
150 cm^2

36. $V = \frac{1}{3}\pi(7^2)(10) =$
$\frac{1}{3}\pi(490) \approx 513.13$ cm^2

37. $A = 2\pi(3^2) + 2\pi(3)(8) =$
$18\pi + 48\pi = 66\pi \approx 207.35$ cm^2

35. The formula for the surface area of a cube with edges of length e is $A = 6e^2$. Find the surface area of a cube with edges of length 5 centimeters.

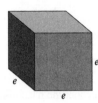

36. The formula for the volume of a cone with radius r and height b is $V = \frac{1}{3}\pi r^2 b$. Find the volume of a cone with a radius of 7 centimeters and a height of 10 centimeters.

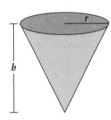

37. The formula for the surface area of a cylinder with radius r and height b is $A = 2\pi r^2 + 2\pi rb$. The $2\pi r^2$ part represents the area of the circular top and bottom, and the $2\pi rb$ part represents the "side" that can be unrolled to form a rectangle. Find the surface area of a cylinder with a radius of 3 centimeters and a height of 8 centimeters.

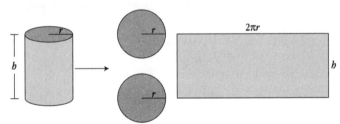

38. The formula for the area of a circle with radius r is $A = \pi r^2$. Tina, Hyung, and Jamal used this formula to estimate the area of a pizza with a diameter of 9 inches. They each found a different area. In a–c, decide whether the student's estimate is reasonable. If the estimate is not reasonable, figure out what mistake the student might have made in his or her calculation.

    a. Tina estimated the area to be about 254 square inches.

    b. Hyung estimated the area to be about 200 square inches.

    c. Jamal estimated the area to be about 64 square inches.

39. The formula for the surface area of a sphere with radius r is $A = 4\pi r^2$.

    a. Find the surface area of a globe with radius 1 foot.

    b. The radius of Earth is about 4000 miles. Find the surface area of Earth.

    c. The radius of the sun is about 430,000 miles. Find the surface area of the sun.

    d. What is the ratio of Earth's radius to the sun's radius?

    e. What is the ratio of Earth's surface area to the sun's surface area?

    f. How does your ratio from part d compare to your ratio from part e?

40. A bacterium colony begins with 5000 bacteria. The population doubles every hour. This pattern of exponential growth can be modeled by the equation $b = 5000(2^t)$, where b is the number of bacteria and t is the number of hours.

    a. What is the population of the colony after 3 hours? After 5 hours?

    b. What mathematical operations did you perform to calculate your answers in part a? In what order did you perform these operations?

38a. Tina probably used 9 as the radius instead of 4.5: $A = \pi(9^2) = \pi(81) \approx 254$ in². (Note: This should alert students to a common error: using diameter instead of radius in the formula for a circle's area.)

38b. Hyung probably squared the product of π and 4.5: $A = (\pi \times 4.5)^2 \approx 200$ in².

38c. Jamal calculated the area correctly: $\pi(4.5^2) \approx 64$ in².

39a. $A = 4\pi(1^2) \approx 12.6$ ft²

39b. $A = 4\pi(4000^2) \approx 200,960,000$ mi²

39c. $A = 4\pi(430,000^2) \approx 2,322,344$ million mi² (**Teaching Tip:** You might want to review scientific notation with your students.)

39d. 4:430 or $\frac{4}{430}$

39e. 200:2,300,000 or $\frac{200}{2,300,000}$ or $\frac{1}{11,500}$

39f. The square of the ratio of the radii is approximately equal to the ratio of the surface areas: $(\frac{4}{430})^2 \approx \frac{1}{11,500}$.

(**Teaching Tip:** Students will not likely arrive at this fact immediately. Class discussion and exploration with a calculator should help.)

40a. $5000(2^3) = 40,000$ bacteria after 3 hours; $5000(2^5) = 160,000$ bacteria after 5 hours

40b. The operations are exponentiation and multiplication; exponentiation is performed before multiplication.

41a. $d = -16(0.1^2) +$
$16(0.1) + 6.5 = -0.16 +$
$1.6 + 6.5 = 7.94$ ft

41b. $d = -16(0.3^2) +$
$16(0.3) + 6.5 = -1.44 +$
$4.8 + 6.5 = 9.86$ ft

41c. $d = -16(1^2) + 16(1) +$
$6.5 = -16 + 16 + 6.5 = 6.5$ ft
(Note: The player's jump is
over; 6.5 ft is the starting
height.)

41d. The operations
are exponentiation, multiplication, and addition;
the exponentiation is done
first, then the multiplication,
and then the addition.
(Note: The multiplication
of numbers not involving
exponents could be done
before the exponentiation.)

Extensions

42a. $y = 0.1(10^2) - 2(10) +$
$25 = 15$ ft, so Julio is
correct. Santha probably
multiplied 0.1 by 10 and
squared the product:
$y = (0.1 \times 10)^2 - 2(10) +$
$25 = 6$ ft.

42b. $y = 0.1(20^2) - 2(20) +$
$25 = 25$ ft, so Donny is
correct. Joyce probably
multiplied 0.1 by 20 and
squared the product:
$y = (0.1 \times 20)^2 - 2(20) +$
$25 = 4 - 40 + 25 = -11$ ft.

---

41. The equation $d = -16t^2 + 16t + 6.5$ represents the distance in feet from the
ground to the top of a basketball player's head t seconds after the player jumps.

   a. Find the distance to the top of the player's head after 0.1 second.

   b. Find the distance to the top of the player's head after 0.3 second.

   c. Find the distance to the top of the player's head after 1 second.

   d. What mathematical operations did you perform to calculate your answers
   in parts a–c? In what order did you perform these operations?

Extensions

42. The equation $y = 0.1x^2 - 2x + 25$
describes the height of a suspension
cable above the bridge it supports
as a function of the distance, x,
from one end of the bridge. All
measurements are in feet.
Several students used
this equation to estimate
the height for different
x values.

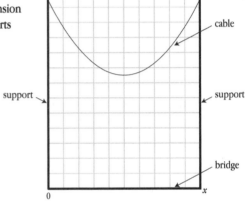

   a. For $x = 10$, Santha
   calculated a height
   of 6 feet, and Julio
   calculated a height
   of 15 feet. Which student is correct? What error do you think the other
   student made?

   b. For $x = 20$, Joyce calculated a height of -11 feet, and Donny calculated
   a height of 25 feet. Which student is correct? What error do you think the
   other student made?

Mathematical Reflections

In this investigation, you evaluated algebraic expressions for given values of the variables. As you worked, you explored the rules for order of operations. These questions will help you summarize what you have learned:

1 **a.** When an expression involves addition, subtraction, and multiplication, in what order should you perform the operations?

b. Illustrate your answer to part a by writing an appropriate expression and evaluating it for specific values of the variables.

2 **a.** When an expression involves division and other operations such as addition, subtraction, and multiplication, in what order should you perform the operations?

b. Illustrate your answer to part a by writing an appropriate expression and evaluating it for specific values of the variables.

3 **a.** When an expression involves exponents and other operations such as addition, subtraction, and multiplication, in what order should you perform the operations?

b. Illustrate your answer to part a by writing an appropriate expression and evaluating it for specific values of the variables.

Think about your answers to these questions, discuss your ideas with other students and your teacher, and then write a summary of your findings in your journal.

3b. To evaluate $\frac{2a^2 + 5}{3 - b^3}$ for $a = 3$ and $b = 2$, perform the exponentiation first, followed by the addition and subtraction and finally the division: $\frac{2(3^2) + 5}{3 - 2^3} = \frac{2(9) + 5}{3 - 8} = \frac{18 + 5}{3 - 8} = \frac{23}{-5} = \frac{-23}{5}$.

Tips for the Linguistically Diverse Classroom

Original Rebus The Original Rebus technique is described in detail in *Getting to Know Connected Mathematics*. Students make a copy of the text before it is discussed. During the discussion, they generate their own rebuses for words they do not understand; the words are made comprehensible through pictures, objects, or demonstrations. Example: Question 1a— Key words for which students might make rebuses are *addition* (+), *subtraction* (–), *multiplication* (×), *order* (1, 2, 3, . . .), *operations* (+, –, ×).

Possible Answers

1a. Perform the multiplication first and then the addition and subtraction, unless the addition or subtraction is in parentheses.

1b. To evaluate $2m + 6 - 7n$ for $m = 5$ and $n = 7$, perform the multiplication and then the addition and subtraction: $2(5) + 6 - 7(7) = 10 + 6 - 49 = {}^-33$.

2a. If the division is indicated by a fraction, perform the operations (if any) in the numerator and the operations (if any) in the denominator, and then divide the result in the numerator by that in the denominator. If an expression involves parentheses, do the operations in the parentheses first.

2b. To evaluate $\frac{2w + 5}{3 - z}$ for $w = 5$ and $z = 1$, do the addition in the numerator and the subtraction in the denominator first, and then perform the division: $\frac{2(5) + 5}{3 - 1} = \frac{10 + 5}{2} = \frac{15}{2} = 7.5$.

To evaluate $(x + 2) \div x$ for $x = 4$, perform the operation inside the parentheses and then the division: $(4 + 2) \div 4 = 6 \div 4 = 1.5$.

3a. For expressions involving exponents, do the exponentiation first, and then follow the order outlined in parts 1 and 2.

3b. See left.

TEACHING THE INVESTIGATION

1.1 • Adding and Multiplying

In this problem, students evaluate a symbolic expression representing the price that groups pay to enter an amusement park. To do this, students need to make sense of the operations of addition and multiplication within the expression. They first evaluate the expression for specific values of the variables and then observe the order in which they performed mathematical operations. To help students develop their intuition about order of operations, it is important to have them *think about, write about,* and *discuss* their observations as they work through the activities.

Launch

Introduce the story of the Water Works amusement park and the equation used to determine admission prices for groups of adults and children. Students are to use the equation $p = 100 + 10a + 8c$ to find group admission prices for various values of a (the number of adults) and c (the number of children). Then they will analyze their work to look for patterns and determine in what order mathematical operations must be performed.

In the problem, students are not instructed to perform multiplication from left to right prior to addition. However, the real-world context and their prior experience with simpler arithmetic and algebraic representations will likely suggest this as a natural procedure.

Have students work in groups of three or four on the problem. Because students need to focus their attention on articulating their sense of the rules governing order of operations, save the follow-up questions until after the summary of the problem.

Explore

Ask each student to make a table. Part A requests that students do their calculations without a calculator to help them focus on the order in which they must multiply and add. However, you may want to allow students to check their calculations, such as 8×80, using a calculator.

As you circulate through the room, look for students who are not performing operations in the correct sequence. Ask questions to assess their understanding and to help them use the problem context to ascertain the logical order.

What information do the numbers 10 and 8 give? *(the number of dollars per adult and child, respectively)*

How can you use this information to find the price for the group? *(multiply 10 by the number of adults and 8 by the number of children, and add these two products to 100)*

Do your results make sense?

Summarize

Groups' results may vary; have them share their answers and their arguments. If they have all done the calculations correctly, ask:

> Why didn't you simply operate from left to right when you calculated the admission price for a particular group?

If there are differences of approach that lead to conflicting answers, discuss the information given by each term in the equation and the sequence of operations they logically suggest.

Part C asks about the information represented by the numbers 100, 10, and 8 in the equation. Once students know that 10 and 8 represent the cost per adult and child, respectively, and that 100 is the fixed price for a group regardless of how many people are in the group, they can use the context to help make sense of the order of operations: multiply the price of an adult ticket by the number of adults, multiply the price of a child's ticket by the number of children, and add these two products to 100.

If the class seems ready, raise the idea of the existence of an established rule for order of operations in expressions that involve addition and multiplication.

When you have finished summarizing the problem, assign the follow-up. In question 2, the probability of rain is expressed as a percent; students may need a reminder to convert percents to decimals or fractions.

Review the follow-up questions. If students' answers vary, ask the class to interpret the numbers and symbols in each expression. The contexts suggest the correct order of operations.

> In each equation, what operations are involved?
>
> In what order should those operations be performed?

Discuss the order of operations that students observed in parts 1d and 2d.

> Does your calculator use the same order of operations that you used in Problem 1.1?

If there are conflicting ideas, you may want to evaluate the numerical expressions on the overhead graphing calculator as students discuss what they see happening.

Part c of questions 1–3 and question 5 are essential for students to develop intuition about the order of operations. As the class discusses these questions, look for any misconceptions or alternative ways to do the computations. For example, to evaluate $40 - 5(3) + 7(5)$, students might combine $^-15$ and 35 and add the result to 40, or they might add 35 to 40 and then subtract 15. The class should reach the general conclusion that multiplication is done before addition or subtraction.

To assess students' understanding of what has been covered, write a final equation involving addition and multiplication on the overhead or the board:

Evaluate $p = 50 - 5a + 4b$ when $a = 9$ and $b = 12$.

As an extra challenge, you might ask:

For what values of a or b will p be negative?

This question encourages students to stand back and make sense of the symbols. The equation can be rewritten, for example, as $p = (50 + 4b) - 5a$, so the value of p will be negative only when $5a$ is greater than $50 + 4b$. If $b = 1$, for example, p will be negative when a is greater than $\frac{54}{5}$.

For the Teacher: Creating a Program for Evaluating an Expression

Some students might enjoy using the program feature of their graphing calculators to check their work. The following program, written for the TI-80 graphing calculator, evaluates the expression $100 + 10a + 8c$.

To create a new program on the TI-80, press PRGM, select NEW, and press ENTER to choose CREATE NEW. Enter a name for the program (the keys will be set to display alphabetic characters), and press ENTER.

Now enter the program commands using the program editor. See your graphing calculator manual for more information.

```
:PRGRAM:PRICE
:DISP "A?"
:INPUT A
:DISP "C?"
:INPUT C
:100+10A+8C→P
:DISP P
```

When you have finished entering the program, press 2nd MODE. To execute the program, press PRGM, select your program, and press ENTER.

Students who enjoy computer programming might be interested to know that complex calculations are often broken down into single-step calculations and the results stored in "dummy" variables. For example, $F = \frac{9}{5}C + 32$ may be expressed as $T_1 = \frac{9}{5}C$ and $F = T_1 + 32$. Students could write such single-step code for $P = 100 + 10a + 8c$.

1.2 • Dividing

By using the context of calculating the average concession profit per park visitor, this problem adds the operation of division to the symbolic expressions that students are analyzing.

Launch

Discuss the context of the problem prior to introducing the equation.

> If you were in charge of the concession stands at the water park, what would probably be the most important factor in predicting the profit the concessions make in one day? *(the number of visitors)*
>
> Do more visitors to the park necessarily mean greater profit? *(In general, as the number of visitors increases, profit will increase.)*

Note that at some point profit would stop increasing; the concession stands would have a maximum capacity.

> Why might it be helpful to find the average concession profit per visitor? *(This information would aid in evaluating the business.)*
>
> How would you find the average concession profit per visitor? *(Compute the daily concession profit and divide it by the number of visitors.)*

Write the equation $P = 2.50V - 500$ on the board.

> This is the equation for the daily concession profit. What do the numbers 2.50 and 500 represent in this equation? *(2.50 represents the average amount a visitor spends at the concessions; 500 represents the fixed cost of operating the concession stands.)*

Divide the equation by V to produce the new equation $A = \frac{2.50V - 500}{V}$.

> This equation represents the average daily concession profit per visitor. Why is the variable V in the numerator and the denominator? *(V represents the number of visitors. It is used in the numerator to determine the total daily profit. It is used in the denominator to divide the total daily profit by the number of visitors to get the* average *daily profit per visitor.)*

End the discussion here to allow students to determine on their own when the division indicated by the fraction bar must be performed. Through their exploration and subsequent sharing of ideas, it should become evident that only when both the numerator and denominator have been evaluated can the division be performed.

Have students work on the problem in groups of three or four. Save the follow-up until after the summary of the problem.

Explore

Ask each student to make a table. Evaluations of expressions should again be done by hand so that students confront decisions about the order in which operations must be done.

If students are not performing operations in the correct sequence, ask questions similar to those in the launch to help them use the context to make sense of the operations.

Summarize

Discuss each part of the problem with the class. When you go over part C, ask students to use their calculators to evaluate the expressions for average per-visitor profit.

> What expressions did you have to enter into your calculator to get the correct answers? Why did you have to use parentheses?

The calculator requires the use of parentheses to isolate the numerator. On paper, students may compute the numerator and then divide by the denominator. In both situations, the subtraction within the parentheses is performed before the division.

Part E offers an opportunity to discuss the various ways to represent division. Ask students to evaluate all three expressions for a few values of V to demonstrate that they produce equivalent answers. You could also suggest a fourth equation, $A = (2.50V - 500)\frac{1}{V}$, and ask whether it is equivalent to the others.

You may want to put a few expressions on the board and ask the class to rewrite and evaluate them. For example, display the expression $\frac{50x - 130}{x}$.

> Write this expression in two different, but equivalent, ways. Evaluate each of your expressions for $x = 10$. *(Each should give an answer of 37.)*

Now write $(3x - 70) \div x$ on the board.

> Why are the parentheses used in this form of the expression? *(to show what part is the numerator)*

> Write this expression in two different, but equivalent, ways. Evaluate each of your expressions for $x = 10$. *(Each should give an answer of ⁻4.)*

> How would you evaluate the expression $6 + 18 \div 3$? Explain your reasoning.

> What is the difference between the expressions $(6 + 18) \div 3$ and $6 + 18 \div 3$? Are they equivalent? Why or why not?

Students might say, based on their experience, that in the first expression the parentheses represent the numerator, so you calculate it and then divide. In the second, you could add 6 and 18 and then divide by 3, or you could divide 18 by 3 and then add 6—which gives a different answer.

> Because of this confusion, mathematicians have established rules for order of operations. They have agreed that division and multiplication are done before addition and subtraction. You can always use parentheses to help avoid confusion.

If students need more review, write $18 \div 3$ on the board and ask what other ways exist to express this division. They may need to see several such examples to be reminded that $18 \div 3 = 18 \times \frac{1}{3}$.

Now assign the follow-up. In the class discussion of these questions, students should reach the following conclusions:

- The rules concerning order of operations that guide the evaluation of algebraic fractions are (1) do the calculations (if any) in the numerator, (2) do the calculations (if any) in the denominator, and (3) divide the resulting numerator by the resulting denominator.

- If division is denoted by multiplication, as in $\frac{1}{V}(2.50V - 500)$, first work within the parentheses and then multiply.

- If division is denoted by the division sign, as in $(2.50V - 500) \div V$, first work within the parentheses and then divide.

1.3 • Working with Exponents

The context of this problem is an arch to be built at the entrance to the water park. The shape of the arch is described by the equation $y = 5x - 0.1x^2$, where y is the height of the arch above a point on the ground x feet from one of the bases of the arch. The problem addresses order of operations in expressions involving exponents.

Launch

Discuss the arch to be built at Water Works. Write the equation of the arch, $y = 5x - 0.1x^2$, on the board or the overhead.

What shape does this equation describe?

Most students should recognize that the equation describes a parabola and be able to make a sketch. They may need prompting to find the maximum point and the x- and y-intercepts.

So, this equation will produce an arch with a parabolic shape.

Display Transparency 1.3A, or sketch the arch on the board. Be sure students understand what the variables in the equation represent.

What does x stand for? (the distance in feet from one base)

What does y stand for? (the height of the arch at that value of x)

Evaluate the expression $5x - 0.1x^2$ for $x = 5$ feet. What does the result represent? (The result is 22.5, which represents the height of the arch in feet above a point 5 feet from one of the bases of the arch.)

Indicate the point (5, 22.5) on the arch.

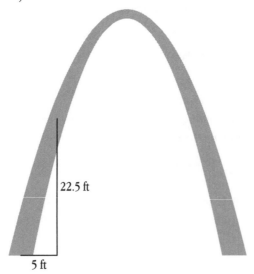

22.5 ft

5 ft

Have students explore the problem and the follow-up in groups of three or four.

Explore

Most of this problem should be a review for the class. Students evaluated quadratic expressions in *Frogs, Fleas, and Painted Cubes*. Now they are asked to make generalizations about the order of operations when an expression containing exponents is evaluated for a specific value of the variable.

Summarize

As students share their answers, look for misconceptions in their reasoning. They should be able to discuss the order of operations involved in the equivalent expressions $5x - 0.1x^2$ and $0.1x(50 - x)$. In the first expression, exponentiation is done first followed by multiplication and

---

For the Teacher: Vocabulary for Discussing Order of Operations

This is a good opportunity to comment on the distinction between a *term* and a *factor*. Informally, *terms* are expressions and quantities that are added or subtracted; *factors* are expressions and quantities that are multiplied. These words are discussed in the development of the distributive property in Investigations 2 and 3.

It will be helpful for students to have a working familiarity with the words *sum, difference, product,* and *quotient* as well as *term* and *factor* in order to be able to articulate the sequence of operations that they observe.

Additionally, you may want to introduce the word *exponentiation* for discussing the operation of raising a quantity to a power.

---

then subtraction. In the second, subtraction within the parentheses is done first, followed by multiplication.

You might ask the class to evaluate each expression for specific values of x using a calculator and then share how they entered the expressions. Students may suggest several correct ways to enter a given expression.

Use the arch equation to help students review quadratic relationships.

> The factored form of the equation for the height of the arch is
> $y = 0.1x(50 - x)$. What does this tell you about the position of the bases
> of the arch? *(The bases of the arch are at the x-intercepts, 0 and 50.)*
> How far apart are the bases of the arch? *(50 feet)*
>
> What is the maximum height of the arch? *[The maximum height of the
> arch occurs halfway between the bases, or 25 feet from either base. The
> maximum height is thus 0.1(25)(50 − 25) = 62.5 feet.]*

Discuss the follow-up questions, which are primarily review. Students should again generalize that exponentiation is done first, followed by multiplication.

Additional Answers

Answers to Problem 1.1

A.

Group Admission Prices

Number of children

		20	40	60	80	100
Number of adults	10	360	520	680	840	1000
	20	460	620	780	940	1100
	30	560	720	880	1040	1200
	40	660	820	980	1140	1300

Answers to Problem 1.2

D. The operations are multiplication, subtraction, and division. Using the equation $A = \frac{2.50V - 500}{V}$, multiply the number of visitors by 2.50, subtract 500 from that product, and divide the resulting difference by the number of visitors.

E. The manager is correct. Division can be indicated with a division sign, ÷, so $(2.50V - 500) \div V$ is equal to $\frac{2.50V - 500}{V}$. And dividing by a number is the same as multiplying by the reciprocal of that number, so $\frac{2.50V - 500}{V} = \frac{1}{V}(2.50V - 500)$. (Note: Students may not use the word *reciprocal*, but they should understand the principle.)

Answers to Problem 1.2 Follow-Up

1. a. $\frac{100 + 3(25)}{25} = \frac{100 + 75}{25} = \frac{175}{25} = 7$

   b. $(100 + 3 \times 25)/25$

2. a. $\frac{3(10)}{4(10) + 3} = \frac{30}{40 + 3} = \frac{30}{43}$

   b. $3 \times 10/(4 \times 10 + 3)$

3. First do the calculations (if any) in the numerator and the calculations (if any) in the denominator. Divide the resulting numerator by the resulting denominator.

ACE Answers

Connections

32a. Possible table:

R	V
0	600
0.20	500
0.40	400
0.60	300
0.80	200
1.00	100

32b.

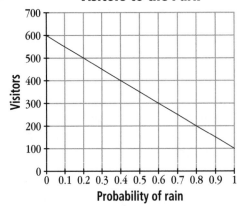

Visitors to the Park

32c. The slope is ⁻500; it shows that the number of visitors decreases as the probability of rain increases. The *y*-intercept is 600; it shows that when the probability of rain is 0, 600 people will visit the park. [**Teaching Tip:** Ask students what the limitations are on the value of *R* and how they affect the graph. *R* is the probability of rain; probabilities cannot be greater than 100% or less that 0%, so the part of the graph that makes sense in this situation is the line segment between (0, 600) and (1, 100).]

33a. Possible table:

V	E
100	150
200	200
300	250
400	300
500	350

33b.

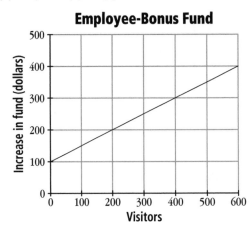

Employee-Bonus Fund

33c. The slope is 0.50; it indicates that for every additional visitor, the bonus fund increases by 50¢. The *y*-intercept is 100; it indicates that the fund will increase by $100 on days when no one visits the park. (**Teaching Tip:** Ask students what part of the graph makes sense in this situation.)

Equivalent Expressions

In their mathematics work this year, students have learned that supporting their answers is important and that there is often more than one way to solve a problem. In this investigation, they have an opportunity to justify, in their own ways, the equivalence of two or more symbolic expressions for the same situation. In addition, the structures of the problems make it inevitable that important properties of numbers, especially the distribute property, will be articulated and applied.

Problem 2.1, Tiling Pools, asks students to find a generalization for the number of square tiles needed to construct a border around a square pool. Students are encouraged to think about the problem in a variety of ways that lead to different, yet equivalent, equations. Problem 2.2, Thinking in Different Ways, poses several equivalent expressions for finding the number of border tiles. Students are asked to describe the reasoning behind each expression and then explain how they know the expressions are equivalent. They also compare graphs and tables of equivalent expressions. In Problem 2.3, Diving In, students investigate the areas of swimming pools that are divided into two sections. They find that the two basic ways of approaching these problems result in two types of expressions, those in factored form and those in expanded form.

By the conclusion of Problem 2.3, students will have developed a strong sense of the distributive property independent of a specific context. In Investigation 3, they will learn the name of the property.

Mathematical and Problem-Solving Goals

- *To informally articulate the distributive property*
- *To apply the distributive property to simplify and compare expressions*
- *To further articulate what it means for two expressions to be equivalent*
- *To judge the equivalency of two or more expressions by examining the reasoning that each represents*
- *To determine the equivalency of two or more expressions by examining tables and graphs*

Materials

Problem	For students	For the teacher
All	Graphing calculators, grid paper, square tiles (optional)	Transparencies: 2.1 to 2.3, overhead graphing calculator, transparent grid, square tiles for the overhead (all optional)
2.2	Large sheets of paper or blank transparencies (optional)	

Launch

- Introduce the idea of finding the number of square tiles required to form a border around a square pool.

- Have pairs work on the problem and follow-up.

Explore

- Have each pair share their reasoning with another pair.

Summarize

- Ask students to use diagrams to explain the reasoning that led to their equations.

- Ask students how they can verify that the various equations are equivalent.

INVESTIGATION 2

Equivalent Expressions

Throughout your work in mathematics this year, you have written symbolic expressions and equations to represent situations involving variables. Because there is usually more than one way to think about a situation, there is often more than one way to express the situation in symbols. For example, consider the perimeter of a rectangle with length L and width W.

Think about this!

Jim says the perimeter of the rectangle above is $2(L + W)$. Lilia says the perimeter is $2L + 2W$. How could you convince the students that their expressions are equivalent?

Since $2(L + W)$ and $2L + 2W$ represent the same quantity, they are **equivalent expressions**. In this investigation, you will look at situations that can be described with several different, but equivalent, expressions, and you will see how each expression represents a unique way of interpreting a situation. You will also learn some methods for showing that two expressions are equivalent.

2.1 Tiling Pools

Hot tubs and in-ground swimming pools are sometimes surrounded by borders of tiles. This drawing shows a square hot tub with sides of length 5 feet surrounded by square border tiles. The border tiles measure 1 foot on each side. A total of 24 tiles are needed for the border.

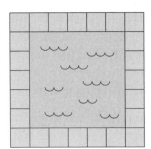

Assignment Choices

ACE questions 1–3 and unassigned choices from earlier problems

Answers to Problem 2.1

A.

Side length (ft)	Number of tiles
1	8
2	12
3	16
4	20
6	28
10	44

B. Some possible equations are listed here; studen may not find all of these at this time. See the "Summarize" section for several ways that students may have reasoned about the problem. Students will revisit this question in Problem 2.

$N = 4s + 4$ $N = s + s + s + s + 4$

$N = 2s + 2(s + 2)$ $N = 4(s + 2) - 4$

$N = (s + 2)^2 - s^2$ $N = 4(s + 1)$

$N = 8 + 4(s - 1)$

C. See the equations in part B. Explanations will vary; students may reason from the geometry of the situation or talk about substituting values of s to show equivalence.

Problem 2.1

In this problem, you will explore this question: If a square pool has sides of length s feet, how many tiles are needed to form the border?

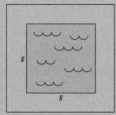

s

s

1 ft

1 ft

border tile

A. Make sketches on grid paper to help you figure out how many tiles are needed for the borders of square pools with sides of length 1, 2, 3, 4, 6, and 10 feet. Record your results in a table.

B. Write an equation for the number of tiles, N, needed to form a border for a square pool with sides of length s feet.

C. Try to write at least one more equation for the number of tiles needed for the border of the pool. How could you convince someone that your expressions for the number of tiles are equivalent?

■ Problem 2.1 Follow-Up

1. Make a table and a graph for each equation you wrote in part a of Problem 2.1. Do the table and the graph indicate that the equations are equivalent? Explain.

2. Is the relationship between the side length of the pool and the number of tiles linear, quadratic, exponential, or none of these? Explain your reasoning.

3. a. Write an equation for the area of the pool, A, in terms of the side length, s.
   b. Is the equation you wrote linear, quadratic, exponential, or none of these? Explain.

4. a. Write an equation for the combined area of the pool and its border, C, in terms of the side length, s.
   b. Is the equation you wrote linear, quadratic, exponential, or none of these? Explain.

Answers to Problem 2.1 Follow-Up

1, 2. See page 33k.

3.   a. $A = s^2$

   b.   The equation is quadratic; explanations will vary. For example, the equation is quadratic because it contains the independent variable squared. The graph of the equation has a parabolic shape that is characteristic of quadratic relationships. A table made from the equation has constant second differences.

4.   a. $C = (s + 2)^2$

   b.   This equation is quadratic as well; explanations will vary. See the possible explanations in the answer to 3b.

Thinking in Different Ways

Launch

- Talk about Takashi's expression and reasoning.

- Decide whether or not to omit expressions that students found in Problem 2.1.

- Have groups of two to four explore the problem and follow-up.

Explore

- Distribute large sheets of paper or blank transparencies for students to make their drawings for sharing later. *(optional)*

Summarize

- Have groups share their reasoning for the various expressions.

- Talk about the follow-up questions.

2.2 Thinking in Different Ways

You and your classmates probably found more than one way to express the number of tiles needed for the border of a square pool. Now you will explore how different ways of thinking about this problem lead to different expressions.

Problem 2.2

Takashi thought of the pool's border as being composed of four 1-by-s rectangles, each made from s tiles, and four corner squares, each made from one tile. He wrote the expression $4s + 4$ to represent the total number of border tiles.

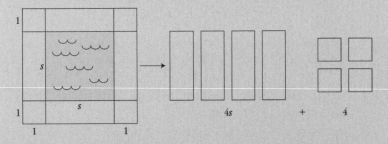

A. Stella wrote the expression $4(s + 1)$ to represent the number of border tiles. Draw a picture that illustrates how Stella might have been thinking about the border of the pool.

B. Jeri wrote the expression $s + s + s + s + 4$ to represent the number of border tiles. Draw a picture that illustrates how Jeri might have been thinking about the border of the pool.

C. Sal wrote the expression $2s + 2(s + 2)$ to represent the number of border tiles. Draw a picture that illustrates how Sal might have been thinking about the border of the pool.

D. Jackie wrote the expression $4(s + 2) - 4$ to represent the number of border tiles. Draw a picture that illustrates how Jackie might have been thinking about the border of the pool.

E. Explain why each expression in parts A–D is equivalent to Takashi's expression.

Answers to Problem 2.2

See page 33k. Note: Students' illustrations and ideas will vary. If all or most of these expressions arose in the discussion of Problem 2.1, you may want to encourage students to use their intuitive sense of the distributive property to show that the expressions are equivalent.

Answers to Problem 2.2 Follow-Up

See page 33l.

■ **Problem 2.2 Follow-Up**

1. Evaluate each of the five expressions given in the problem for $s = 10$. Can you conclude from your results that all the expressions are equivalent? Explain your reasoning.

2. Make a table and a graph for each of the five expressions. Do the tables and the graphs indicate that the expressions are equivalent? Explain.

 2.3 **Diving In**

Swimming pools are sometimes divided into sections that are used for different purposes. For example, a pool may have a section for lap swimming and a section for diving, or a section for experienced swimmers and a section for small children.

In this problem, you will investigate ways to express the surface area of the water in several divided pools. The problem illustrates an important and useful mathematical property that you will use throughout the remainder of this unit.

Problem 2.3

Below are four designs for pools with swimming and diving sections. For each design, show two methods for calculating the total surface area of the water. Then tell which method is more efficient. That is, tell which method requires fewer mathematical operations.

A.
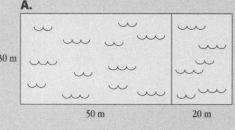

B.
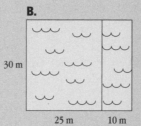

C.
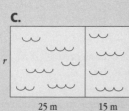

D.
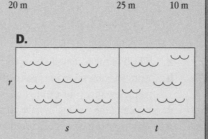

Diving In

Grouping: *individuals, then small groups*

Launch

■ Ask students what relationship they have noticed among the equivalent expressions for the number of border tiles.

■ Have students begin work on the problem individually.

Explore

■ Have students discuss their ideas in pairs and finish the problem.

Summarize

■ Talk about the problem, reviewing the terms *factored form* and *expanded form*.

■ Have pairs do the follow-up.

■ Lead a discussion in which students share their informal understanding of the distributive property.

Answers to Problem 2.3

Students' choices for which method is more efficient will vary. Some methods require three mathematical operations; others require only two.

A. $30(50) + 30(20) = 1500 + 600 = 2100$ m²

$30(50 + 20) = 30(70) = 2100$ m²

B. $30(25) + 30(10) = 750 + 300 = 1050$ m²

$30(25 + 10) = 30(35) = 1050$ m²

C. $r(25) + r(15) = 25r + 15r = 40r$

$r(25 + 15) = r(40) = 40r$

D. $r(s) + r(t) = rs + rt$

$r(s + t)$

Assignment Choices

ACE questions 4–18, 20–22, and unassigned choices from earlier problems

Problem 2.3 Follow-Up

As you worked on Problem 2.3, you found two equivalent expressions for the surface area of the water in each pool. For example, to find the surface area of the pool in part A, you might have multiplied the length of the entire pool by its width to get $30(50 + 20)$, and you might have added the areas of the two sections to get $30(50) + 30(20)$. The expressions $30(50 + 20)$ and $30(50) + 30(20)$ are equivalent. We say that $30(50 + 20)$ is in **factored form** and $30(50) + 30(20)$ is in **expanded form**.

1. Use the drawings below to answer parts a–d.

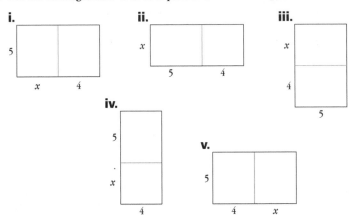

i. **ii.** **iii.**

iv.

v.

a. Which of the rectangles have an area of $5(4 + x)$?

b. Write an expression in expanded form that is equivalent to $5(4 + x)$. Explain how you know that your expression is equivalent to $5(4 + x)$.

c. Which of the rectangles have an area of $5x + 4x$?

d. Write an expression in factored form that is equivalent to $5x + 4x$. Explain how you know that your expression is equivalent to $5x + 4x$.

Answers to Problem 2.3 Follow-Up

1, 2. See page 33m.

3. a. $6 + 1.5x$

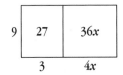

b. $3x + 5x$

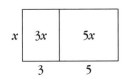

4. a. $9(3 + 4x)$

b. $x(2 + 7)$

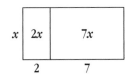

2. **a.** Draw a diagram that uses areas of rectangles to illustrate that $5x + 10$ and $5(x + 2)$ are equivalent.

   b. Use tables or graphs to show that $5x + 10$ and $5(x + 2)$ are equivalent.

3. Write an expression in expanded form that is equivalent to the given expression. Draw a diagram to illustrate the equivalence.

   a. $1.5(4 + x)$

   b. $x(3 + 5)$

4. Write an expression in factored form that is equivalent to the given expression. Draw a diagram to illustrate the equivalence.

   a. $27 + 36x$

   b. $2x + 7x$

5. Express the area of the purple rectangle in both factored form and expanded form.

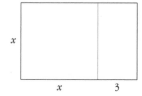

6. **a.** Draw a rectangle whose area can be represented by the expression $x(5 + x)$.

   b. Write an expression in expanded form that is equivalent to $x(5 + x)$.

7. As you worked on the border-tile and pool-area problems in this investigation, you found equivalent ways to express a quantity.

   a. Use what you have learned to write some expressions that are equivalent to $4x + 6$.

   b. Use what you have learned to write some expressions that are equivalent to $x^2 + 4x$.

   c. What general rules have you discovered that can help you write equivalent expressions?

5. factored form: $x(x + 3)$; expanded form: $x^2 + 3x$

6. a.  b. $5x + x^2$

7. a. Possible answer: $6 + 4x$, $2(2x + 3)$, $2(3 + 2x)$

   b. Possible answer: $4x + x^2$, $x(4 + x)$, $x(x + 4)$

   c. Possible answer: You can change the order in which terms are added or factors are multiplied. If two numbers are multiplied and one is a sum, you can multiply the single factor by each term in the sum. You can also pull out a common factor from each term in a sum.

Answers

Applications

1a. 2(10) + 2(5) + 4 = 34 tiles

1b. Possible expressions: 2*L* + 2*W* + 4, 2(*L* + 1) + 2(*W* + 1), 2(*L* + 2) + 2*W*, 2*L* + 2(*W* + 2)

1c. See below right.

2a. 4(7) + 4(0.5) = 30 tiles

2b. Possible answer: *N* = 4*s* + 2, *N* = 4(*s* + 0.5)

Applications • Connections • Extensions

As you work on these ACE questions, use your calculator whenever you need it.

Applications

1. **a.** How many 1-foot-square tiles are needed to form a border for a pool that is 10 feet long and 5 feet wide?

b. Write an expression for the number of border tiles needed for a pool that is *L* feet long and *W* feet wide.

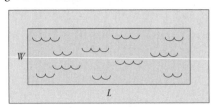

c. Write a different expression for the number of tiles needed. Explain why your expressions are equivalent.

2. A square hot tub has sides of length *s* feet. A border is created by placing square tiles measuring 1 foot on each side along the edges of the tub and triangular tiles in the corners. The triangular tiles were made by cutting square tiles in half.

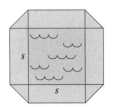

a. If the hot tub has sides of length 7 feet, how many square tiles are needed to make the border?

b. Write two equations for the number of square tiles, *N*, needed to build this type of border for a square tub with sides of length *s* feet.

26 **Say It with Symbols**

1c. See part b for some expressions; explanations will vary. Students might draw sketches; for example:

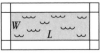 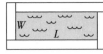 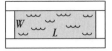 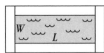

2*L* + 2*W* + 4   2(*L* + 1) + 2(*W* + 1)   2(*L* + 2) + 2*W*   2*L* + 2(*W* + 2)

They might substitute values for *L* and *W* in the expressions; for example, when *W* = 2 and *L* = 3:

2*L* + 2*W* + 4 = 2(3) + 2(2) + 4 = 14   2(*L* + 1) + 2(*W* + 1) = 2(4) + 2(3) = 14
2(*L* + 2) + 2*W* = 2(5) + 2(2) = 14   2*L* + 2(*W* + 2) = 2(2) + 2(4) = 14

Students might also generate tables for their expressions. (Note: Generating tables for all possible values is impossible, so we can't say with certainty that the expressions are equivalent using this method. However, for students at this stage, identical tables indicate that the expressions are equivalent. Since there are two independent variables, making graphs would be difficult.)

26 **Investigation 2**

3. A rectangular pool is L feet long and W feet wide. A border is created by placing square tiles measuring 1 foot on each side along the edges of the pool and triangular tiles in the corners. The triangular tiles were made by cutting square tiles in half.

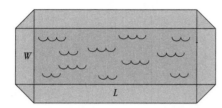

    a. If the pool is 30 feet long and 20 feet wide, how many square tiles are needed to make the border?

    b. Write two equations for the number of square tiles, N, needed to make this type of border for a pool L feet long and W feet wide.

In 4 and 5, write two expressions, one in factored form and one in expanded form, for the area of the purple rectangle.

4.

5.

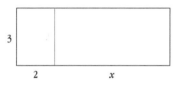

3a. 2(30) + 2(20) + 2 = 102 tiles

3b. Possible answer: $N = 2L + 2W + 2$, $N = 2(L + 0.5) + 2(W + 0.5)$

4. factored form: 3(2 + 5), expanded form: 3(2) + 3(5)

5. factored form: 3(2 + x), expanded form: 3(2) + 3(x)

6a. Rectangles i and iv have an area of 6(x + 1).

6b. 6x + 6

7a. Rectangles i, iii, and v have an area of 5(2x).
In i, x + x is equal to 2x.
In iii, 4 + 1 is equal to 5.
In v, there are 5 subparts with an area of 2x, or 5(2x).

7b. Possible answers:
2x + 2x + 2x + 2x + 2x,
2(5x), 5x + 5x, 10x

6. a. Which rectangles below have an area of 6(x + 1)?

   b. Write an expression in expanded form that is equivalent to 6(x + 1).

i.

ii.

iv.

iii.

7. a. Which rectangles below have an area of 5(2x)? Explain your answer.

   b. Write an expression that is equivalent to 5(2x).

i.

ii.

iii.

iv.

v.

8. a. Is $3x + 8$ equivalent to $3(x + 8)$? Explain.

b. Is $3(x + 8)$ equivalent to $3(8 + x)$? Explain.

c. Is $3x + 8$ equivalent to $8 + 3x$? Explain.

In 9–12, write an expression that is equivalent to the given expression. If the given expression is in factored form, write an expression in expanded form. If the given expression is in expanded form, write an expression in factored form. Draw a diagram to illustrate the equivalence.

9. $4(x + 1)$ **10.** $16x + 8$

11. $3(2x + 5)$ **12.** $x^2 + 3x$

In 13–18, tell whether the expressions are equivalent, and explain how you know.

13. $2x + 11x$ and $13x$ **14.** $x + 3.5x$ and $3.5x$

15. $5(x + 12)$ and $5x + 12$ **16.** $7x$ and $6x + x$

17. $2L + 12$ and $2(1 + L + 5)$ **18.** $3R + 7 + 5R$ and $8R + 7$

19. Franklin's younger sister Taj and her friend Meredith are selling cookies for their girls' club. The cookies sell for $2.50 a box. For each case below, show two methods for calculating the girls' combined income.

a. Taj sells 76 boxes and Meredith sells 49 boxes.

b. Taj sells 43 boxes and Meredith sells 57 boxes.

c. Taj sells x boxes and Meredith sells y boxes.

9. $4(x + 1) = 4x + 4$ **10.** $16x + 8 = 8(2x + 1)$ **11.** $3(2x + 5) = 6x + 15$

          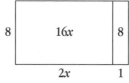   

8a. No; the area model shows that $3(x + 8)$ is equivalent to $3x + 24$, which is not equivalent to $3x + 8$.

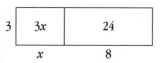

8b. Yes; $3(x + 8)$ is equivalent to $3(8 + x)$ because the order in which two numbers are added does not affect the result. (Note: Some students may have heard of the commutative property of addition. The name is not important at this time, but students should know that the order in which two numbers are added does not matter.)

8c. Yes; $3x + 8$ is equivalent to $8 + 3x$ because the order in which two numbers are added does not affect the result.

9–11. See below left.

12. $x^2 + 3x = x(x + 3)$

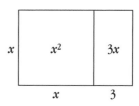

13–18. See page 33n.

19a. $2.50(76 + 49)$ and $2.50(76) + 2.50(49)$

19b. $2.50(43 + 57)$ and $2.50(43) + 2.50(57)$

19c. $2.50(x + y)$ and $2.50x + 2.50y$

20. Possible answer: Sanjay's expression 20(30 + 15) does not take the L-shape of the pool into account; the area of the small section on the upper right, 5(15), must be subtracted from his expression. The actual area is 20(45) − 5(15) = 825 m².

Connections

21. See below right.

22. factored form: $(x + 2)(x + 4)$; expanded form: $x^2 + 2x + 4x + 8$, or $x^2 + 6x + 8$

---

20. Sanjay did the following calculation to compute the surface area of the water in his swimming pool:

$$\text{surface area} = 20(30 + 15) = 20(45) = 900 \text{ m}^2$$

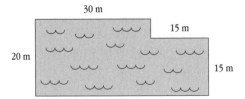

Is Sanjay's calculation correct? If so, explain his reasoning. If not, explain the mistake in his thinking.

Connections

21. A square has sides of length x centimeters. A new rectangle is created by increasing one dimension of the square by 2 centimeters and increasing the other dimension by 3 centimeters. Write two equivalent expressions, one in factored form and one in expanded form, for the area of the new rectangle. Draw a picture to illustrate the equivalence.

22. Write two expressions, one in factored form and one in expanded form, for the area of the purple rectangle below.

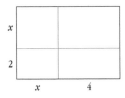

---

21. factored form: $(x + 2)(x + 3)$; expanded form: $x^2 + 2x + 3x + 6$, or $x^2 + 5x + 6$

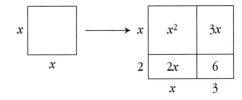

23. A circular hot tub with a radius of 4 feet is surrounded by a border 1 foot wide.

    a. What is the surface area of the water?

    b. What is the area of the border?

    c. Write an expression for the surface area of the water in a circular pool with a radius of r feet.

    d. Write an expression for the area of a 1-foot border around a circular pool with a radius of r feet.

24. The dimensions of the pool below are in feet.

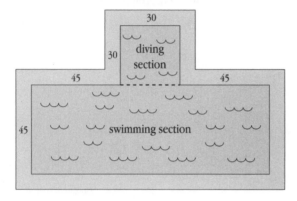

    a. How many square tiles measuring 1 foot on a side are needed to create a border for the pool?

    b. What is the surface area of the water?

    c. The swimming section is 4 feet deep and the diving section is 10 feet deep. What is the volume of the pool?

    d. The pool is filled at the rate of 600 cubic feet per hour. How long does it take to fill the pool?

Investigation 2: Equivalent Expressions   **31**

23a. surface area of water = $\pi(4)^2 = 16\pi \approx 50$ ft²

23b. area of border = $\pi(5^2) - \pi(4^2) = 25\pi - 16\pi = 9\pi \approx 28$ ft²

23c. surface area of water = πr^2

23d. area of border = $\pi(r + 1)^2 - \pi r^2$, or $2\pi r - 1$

24a. 394 tiles; Students will calculate this in various ways, for example: $6(45) + 4(30) + 4$, or $4(45 + 1) + 2(45) + 4(30)$, or $4(45) + (45 + 30 + 45) + 4 + 3(30)$.

24b. 6300 ft²; Students will calculate this in various ways, for example: $2(45^2) + 30(30 + 45)$, or $2(45^2) + 30^2 + 30(45)$, or $45(45 + 30 + 45) + 30^2$.

24c. 30,600 ft³; Students will calculate this in various ways, for example: $4(45)(45 + 30 + 45) + 10(30^2)$, or $4(2)(45^2) + 4(45)(30) + 10(30^2)$, or $4(45^2) + 4(45)(30) + 4(45^2) + 10(30^2)$.

24d. It will take 30,600 ft³ ÷ 600 ft³/h = 51 h to fill the pool.

Extensions

25a. For $s = 1$, 8 tiles are needed. For $s = 2$, $8 + 4$ tiles are needed. For $s = 3$, $8 + 4 + 4$ tiles are needed. Thus, for any s, the number of tiles needed is equal to 8 plus $(s - 1)$ fours, or $8 + 4(s - 1)$.

25b. Susan's expression is equivalent to Takashi's expression, $4s + 4$. Explanations will vary; they may be based on tables, graphs, the substitution of specific values of s, the correctness of the expressions, or the fact that $4(s - 1)$ is the same as $4s - 4$ and thus $8 + 4(s - 1)$ is the same as $8 + 4s - 4$, or $4s + 4$.

Extensions

25. Susan wanted to write an expression for the number of tiles needed to make a border for a square pool with sides of length s feet. She made a table for pools with sides of length 1, 2, 3, 4, and 5 feet and used a pattern in her table to write the expression $8 + 4(s - 1)$.

Side length	1	2	3	4	5
Tiles needed	8	12	16	20	24

a. What pattern did Susan see in her table?

b. Is Susan's expression for the number of tiles equivalent to Takashi's expression in Problem 2.2? Explain why or why not.

Mathematical Reflections

In this investigation, you looked at situations that could be described by different, but equivalent, expressions. These questions will help you summarize what you have learned:

1 What do we mean when we say that the expressions $4n + 4$ and $4(n + 1)$ are *equivalent*? Make a diagram, a table, and a graph to illustrate that the expressions are equivalent.

2 **a.** Write $5x + 8x$ in factored form.

b. Write $5(x + 7)$ in expanded form.

c. How can you tell whether an expression is in expanded form or factored form?

3 **a.** Use drawings, graphs, tables, or some other method to show that $5(2x)$ is equivalent to $2x(5)$.

b. Use drawings, graphs, tables, or some other method to show that $5 + 2x$ is equivalent to $2x + 5$.

c. Make a drawing to show why $5(10) + 2$ is equivalent to $50 + 2$ but not equivalent to $5(10 + 2)$.

4 As you worked with equivalent expressions in this investigation, what patterns did you observe that you could use to show that other expressions are equivalent?

Think about your answers to these questions, discuss your ideas with other students and your teacher, and then write a summary of your findings in your journal.

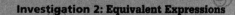

Possible Answers

1. See page 33n.

2a. $x(5 + 8)$, or $(5 + 8)x$

2b. $5x + 35$

2c. *Factored form* indicates a product of two or more factors; it is related to multiplying the dimensions of a rectangle to find its area. *Expanded form* indicates the sum of two or more quantities; it is related to adding the areas of the subparts of a rectangle.

3. See page 33o.

4. If an expression is in factored form, one of the factors can be multiplied by each term in the sum in the parentheses. In the expression $a(b + c)$, each term in the second factor, $b + c$, can be multiplied by a, resulting in $ab + ac$. If an expression is in expanded form, a common factor, if it exists, can be factored from each term. Thus, $ab + ac = a(b + c)$. (Students may also use numerical examples.)

Tips for the Linguistically Diverse Classroom

Diagram Code The Diagram Code technique is described in detail in *Getting to Know Connected Mathematics*. Students use a minimal number of words and drawings, diagrams, or symbols to respond to questions that require writing. Example: Question 2c—A student might respond to this question by writing word *product* and the example $(x + 4)(x + 2)$ under the heading *Factored*, and the word *sum* and the example $x^2 + 5x$ under the heading *Expanded*.

TEACHING THE INVESTIGATION

2.1 • Tiling Pools

In *Thinking with Mathematical Models; Growing, Growing, Growing;* and *Frogs, Fleas, and Painted Cubes;* and in the grade 7 unit *Moving Straight Ahead,* students explored ways in which relationships can be expressed in tables, graphs, and equations. The contextual clues or the patterns in tables or graphs were usually so influential in the construction of the equation that only one version of the equation emerged. In this problem, students are deliberately presented with situations in which contextual clues can be interpreted in several ways to produce different equations. Students are then asked to justify, in informal ways, the equivalence of these equations.

Launch

Talk with the class about the "Think about this!" feature on the opening page of Investigation 2. Ask students to justify why both expressions for the rectangle's perimeter, $2(L + W)$ and $2L + 2W$, are correct. Students may offer examples or talk generally about the dimensions and perimeter of any rectangle. Don't make an issue of the common factor of 2 at this point; focus on the equivalence of the expressions in terms of the context rather than proposing an argument that rests on numerical properties or symbol manipulation.

To introduce Problem 2.1, construct a model of a square pool with sides of length 5 units using transparent square tiles or draw a square pool on the board or a transparent grid. Tell the class that the pool has sides of length 5 feet. Explain that you want to make a border around the pool from 1-foot-square tiles.

> How many square tiles would it take to make a complete border for
> this pool? *(24 tiles)*

Be sure students recognize that although the sides of the pool measure 5 feet, the number of tiles needed to surround the pool is not 20; the four corner tiles bring the total to 24.

Briefly discuss these questions:

> What is the area of the pool? *($5 \times 5 = 25$ ft²)*
>
> What is the area of the pool *plus* the area of the border? *($7 \times 7 = 49$ ft²)*
>
> What is the perimeter of the border?

Some students confuse perimeter with the number of border tiles. The perimeter is $7 \times 4 = 28$ feet.

> Is there an efficient way to calculate the number of border tiles needed
> for a square pool, no matter what the lengths of the sides of the pool are?

Explain that students will investigate this question by analyzing square pools of different sizes.

Have students work in pairs on the problem and the follow-up. Distribute grid paper, and make square tiles available for students who want to use them to model pools and borders.

Explore

Having students articulate how they visualize the situation in Problem 2.1 will help them to make the transition to interpreting the reasoning represented by the symbols in Problem 2.2. Different ways of reasoning about the problem lead to different strategies, which in turn result in different equations. Encourage students to find more than one way to reason. Problem 2.2 presents several ways of thinking about this situation, some of which students will have already discovered.

Students may need help using parentheses in their equations. If you see students who cannot communicate their ideas in writing, you might talk with them about the use of parentheses. Students will work more with this idea in Problem 2.3.

The primary objective of Problem 2.1 is that students be able to justify to their classmates that the expressions they develop to represent the number of tiles are equivalent. It is essential that students articulate their reasoning. Have each pair of students explain to another pair how they thought about the problem to write their equations. Asking them to explain their thinking in writing would also be helpful.

Summarize

Ask students to write their equations on the board until all the equations that the class has generated are represented. For each equation, ask the class:

Can you explain the reasoning that was used to arrive at this equation?

For any equations that the class cannot decipher, ask the students who wrote them to use diagrams to explain their thinking and how the parts of the equation relate to the elements of the problem. Students' explanations might be noted on the board where they can be amended if necessary. Students may be reasoning from numerical examples or from a sketch; verbal and graphical arguments are sufficient at this stage. As students gain more experience with the distributive and commutative properties, they will see ways to rewrite equations to produce equations in different forms.

Students' equations probably include some of the following:

- $N = 4s + 4$
- $N = s + s + s + s + 4$
- $N = 2s + 2(s + 2)$
- $N = 4(s + 2) - 4$
- $N = (s + 2)^2 - s^2$
- $N = 4(s + 1)$
- $N = 8 + 4(s - 1)$

Don't try to get all of these equations at this time. *This question is revisited in Problem 2.2, in which students are asked to draw pictures to represent the thinking that is captured in several different expressions to show that they are equivalent.*

Following are some of the ways students may have reasoned about the number of border tiles. If students do not offer all these ideas, that's fine; they will explore several methods in Problem 2.2.

- They may have considered the four sides first and then added the corner tiles, resulting in the equation $N = 4s + 4$.

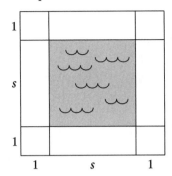

$$N = 4\left(1\underbrace{\boxed{}}_{s}\right) + 4\left(1\boxed{}_{1}\right)$$

- They may have thought about adding the four long strips along the sides and then subtracting the four corner tiles that are counted twice, resulting in the equation $N = 4(s + 2) - 4$.

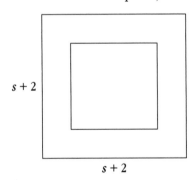

$$N = 4\left(1\underbrace{\boxed{}}_{s+2}\right) - 4\left(1\boxed{}_{1}\right)$$

- They may have reasoned that the number of border tiles is equal to the difference between the areas of the two squares, resulting in the equation $N = (s + 2)^2 - s^2$.

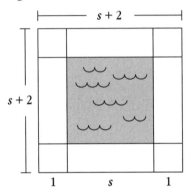

- They may have divided the border into four rectangles with dimensions $s + 1$ and 1, resulting in the equation $N = 4(s + 1)$.

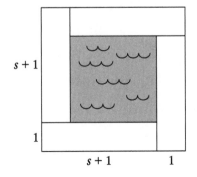

$$N = 4\left(1\underbrace{\boxed{}}_{s+1}\right)$$

■ They may have seen the following pattern in their table: To find the number of border tiles, add 1 to the side length and then multiply by 4, or $N = 4(s + 1)$.

s	N
1	8
2	12
3	16
4	20
5	24
6	28
7	32

■ They may have observed this pattern in the table: For $s = 1$, $N = 8$. For $s = 2$, $N = 8 + 4$. For $s = 3$, $N = 8 + 4 + 4$. For $s = 4$, $N = 8 + 4 + 4 + 4$. Thus, for any s, N is equal to 8 plus $(s - 1)$ fours, or $N = 8 + 4(s - 1)$.

By reasoning about the geometric patterns, students may find other ways to represent the number of border tiles but have trouble expressing their thinking symbolically. Encourage them to try to represent their ideas with drawings. You could leave their explanations as diagrams with descriptions and then return to the symbolic representations after Problem 2.3, which begins the development of the distributive property.

The summary of this problem can lead into the launch of Problem 2.2.

How can we show that all of these expressions for the number of tiles are equivalent?

Some students will probably check the equivalence for a few values of s and argue that if two answers are correct, the expressions must be equivalent. Some may apply geometric reasoning by using diagrams to illustrate the equivalence.

Follow-up question 1 offers another way to check the equivalence of the expressions: creating and comparing tables and graphs of the related equations. Students may be surprised that equations that appear quite different can have identical graphs and tables. Making graphs for different, but equivalent, equations reinforces what students have learned about equivalent representations. You might ask students how they could predict the shape of the graph from the equations or the tables.

In follow-up questions 2–4, students are asked whether given equations are linear, quadratic, or exponential, which reviews relationships that students have studied in previous units.

As a wrap-up to the problem, you could pose ACE question 1, in which students investigate a tile border around a rectangular pool. Let students work on the problem in pairs and share their answers with the class. Be sure they connect each part of the symbolic expression with their conceptualization of the situation and that they have attempted to explain why two different expressions are equivalent. (In this problem, using graphs or tables is problematic because of the number of variables.) Once several expressions have been produced, ask:

Use one of these expressions to find the number of tiles in the border of a pool 37 feet long and 19 feet wide (or other dimensions too great to be conveniently sketched on grid paper and counted).

This will encourage students to generalize. They should all find the same number of tiles. When students have had time to think about this question, ask them to write their own definitions for equivalent expressions.

2.2 • Thinking in Different Ways

Students have modeled geometric situations symbolically and have learned that expressions that look different may actually be equivalent. Now they are asked to connect given expressions to ways of thinking about a situation. The goal is for them to make sense of an expression by relating groups of symbols within that expression to the physical situation. In Problem 2.3, students will generalize their ideas and show that expressions are equivalent using the distributive and commutative properties, which are formally named in Investigation 3.

Launch

Some of the issues raised in this problem may have already been addressed in the class discussion of Problem 2.1. Depending on how successful your class was in finding different ways to reason about the number of border tiles, you may be able to shorten the time spent on this problem.

> In the last problem, we found several symbolic expressions for the number of tiles needed for the border of a square pool. Can you tell from examining another student's expression how he or she reasoned about the situation?
>
> If two students think about a problem in very different ways and both ways make sense to you, how else can you tell if their expressions are equivalent?

Read the description of Takashi's reasoning with the class. The illustration in the student edition and on Transparency 2.2A will help to connect Takashi's expression, $4s + 4$, to parts of the diagram. Make sure everyone can see the four 1-by-s rectangles and the four corner squares. You may want to color the four corner squares to help students understand the diagram.

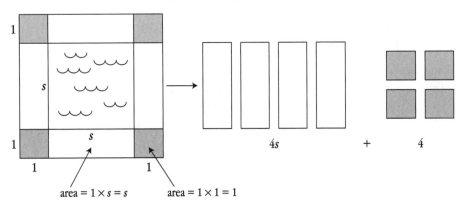

$$4s \qquad + \qquad 4$$

area $= 1 \times s = s$ area $= 1 \times 1 = 1$

On the board, list the four other expressions given in the problem. Explain to students that they are to describe the reasoning someone might have used to derive each expression. If any of the expressions were generated by your students in Problem 2.1, include them for review or simply omit them.

Have students work on the problem and the follow-up in groups of two to four.

Explore

You might have students work on part A individually and, when they have all had a chance to draw a diagram to illustrate Stella's expression, share their pictures and explanations in their groups.

Consider having some groups make their sketches on large sheets of paper to post around the room, which would help those having difficulty and create a spot for students to demonstrate their methods for each expression during the class summary. The drawings could be revisited after the distributive property has been developed in Problem 2.3 or named in the beginning of Investigation 3; students could use them to show equivalence among the expressions.

You might also ask several groups to draw their graphs and tables from follow-up question 2, along with the related expressions and diagrams, on blank transparencies or large sheets of paper, for sharing in the summary.

Summarize

Have groups share their ideas about the reasoning that would lead to each expression. Then ask:

What are the advantages of each representation?

Students may say that Takashi's and Stella's expressions are the easiest to use and that the other expressions represent the area in ways that are easy to understand but are not as easy to use. Explain that when students want to calculate a value and have equivalent expressions from which to choose, they can use whichever is the most convenient.

Ask students to share their answers to part E. Helping students articulate and represent their reasoning about the equivalence of the various expressions will build a foundation for their future work with symbolic reasoning and algebraic manipulation.

Follow-up question 1 asks students to evaluate each expression for $s = 10$. They should find the same result for each expression.

Is one example enough to prove that the expressions are equivalent? *(One example or one point on a graph is not enough, as there is an infinite number of solutions.)*

If students say yes, one example is enough, you may want to write these equations on the board and ask the questions that follow:

$$y = 2x + 1 \qquad\qquad y = x + 2$$

Find *y* when *x* = 1. *(In each equation, y = 3.)*

Find *y* when *x* = 3. *(In the first equation, y = 7; in the second, y = 5.)*

Would it have been a good idea to conclude from our first substitution that the expressions were equivalent? *(no)*

You might quickly sketch the graphs of the two equations and show that they intersect at the point (1, 3). This point lies on both graphs and is thus a solution to both equations.

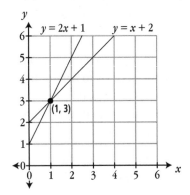

In the next problem, you will develop rules about symbolic expressions that will give you another way to show equivalence.

If students have drawn their graphs on transparencies or large sheets of paper, have them display and compare them.

Notice that some of these graphs have different scales from the majority and that the tables don't all show the same sets of points.

How can we tell whether two graphs or two tables are the same even when they aren't exactly alike?

Help the class understand that when we make tables and graphs for such relationships, it is impossible to list all the pairs of points or to draw the entire graph. We can't prove equivalence by comparing these tables and graphs, but we can look at several values and be reasonably certain of it. Students might discuss whether the parts of the graphs and tables that are showing are sufficient to suggest equivalence.

The fact that tables and graphs are not complete representations of relationships is one motivation for using the properties of real numbers to demonstrate that expressions are equivalent. By applying these properties, we can be absolutely certain of equivalence.

In Investigation 3, students work with the distributive property of real numbers. They can then return to the set of expressions in Problem 2.2 and apply the distributive property to demonstrate their equivalence:

- $4(s + 1) = 4s + 4$
- $2s + 2(s + 2) = 2s + 2s + 4 = 4s + 4$
- $s + s + s + s + 4 = 4s + 4$
- $4(s + 2) - 4 = 4s + 8 - 4 = 4s + 4$

2.3 • Diving In

In this problem, students analyze swimming pools that are divided into two sections. They calculate the total surface area of the water in two ways: by finding the surface area of the pool as a whole and by finding the sum of the surface areas of each section. The group discussion about these methods and their efficiency will help students further develop their intuition about equivalent expressions.

Launch

By the conclusion of this problem, students will have acquired a strong sense of the distributive property independent of a specific context. This is a significant moment in the development of their understanding of algebra. They have seen and used contextual clues and patterns in tables and graphs to reason with and about mathematical models. Now they will learn to manipulate equation models to answer new questions and gain new insights. The symbolic rearrangement dealt with in the distributive property—multiplying through by a common factor or factoring out a common factor—is the basis for many other algebraic-manipulation skills.

To introduce the problem, display or write on the board the various equivalent expressions that were explored in Problems 2.1 and 2.2. Then ask:

> Look carefully at these symbolic expressions. Do you see any relationships between any two particular expressions?

Depending on their level of understanding, students may note that certain pairs of expressions contain the same numbers or that, for example, in the expression $s + s + s + s + 4$, the four s's can be combined, resulting in $4s + 4$.

> Be on the lookout for relationships among the equivalent expressions that you will write in Problem 2.3.

Have students begin work on the problem individually. Save the follow-up until after the problem has been summarized.

Explore

Having students work individually gives everyone a chance to discover the multiple ways in which the areas of the pools can be conceptualized. This problem is rich in ways to reason about the situation. If students move too quickly into groups, one student may propose a strategy that makes it more difficult for the other group members to think about other ways of reasoning.

Once students have had sufficient time to think about the questions, have them discuss their ideas with partners. Conceptualizing the problem is not the same as clearly articulating that conceptualization. Help students recognize and work on their strengths and weaknesses in these areas.

Have students do the follow-up questions individually or in pairs after the summary of the problem.

Summarize

Ask students to summarize the methods they used to calculate the total surface area of the water in the pool. They will probably suggest two methods:

■ Calculate the surface area of each section by multiplying the length by the width, and add the two products.

■ Add the lengths of the two sections, and multiply that sum by the common width.

> What are the advantages of each method? *(Some methods are more efficient; some are easier to understand.)*

To review the terms *factored form* and *expanded form*, apply them to the two expressions students derived for the surface area of one of the pools. For example:

> The surface area of pool B can be expressed as 30(25 + 10). This is a product of two factors, 30 and 25 + 10, and is called the *factored form* of the expression.

> The surface area can also be expressed as 30(25) + 30(10). This is the sum of two quantities, or *terms,* 30(25) and 30(10), and is called the *expanded form* of the expression.

> What is the surface area of pool C in expanded form? *[r(25) + r(15)]* In factored form? *[r(25 + 15)]*

Have the class work on the follow-up questions in pairs, and encourage them to articulate their reasoning about the expressions and the area models with their partners. Some students will be able to see many relationships among symbols without drawing intermediate sketches.

Summarize the follow-up by having students share their answers to the questions below.

> What pattern can you see in moving between an expression in factored form and an expression in expanded form? *(To move from factored form to expanded form, you multiply the factor outside of the parentheses by each term in the parentheses.)*

To help students feel comfortable with intuitively applying or using the distributive property, ask this question:

> Can you give a real-life example that demonstrates that these two forms are equivalent?

Students may make up examples and check that the arithmetic gives the same answers. If they have trouble, you might offer an example in a convincing context. For example, if a movie ticket costs \$3.75 and popcorn costs \$1.75, the total cost of an excursion to the movies for five people is $5(\$3.75 + \$1.75)$, or $5 \times \$3.75 + 5 \times \$1.75$.

The expanded expression in question 4b is $2x + 7x$. You might ask the class how the terms $2x$ and $7x$ are similar. Give them a few more pairs of like terms, and ask them to describe how they can add them. An area model can be used to illustrate the equivalence between $2x + 7x$ and $(2 + 7)x$. The area model also shows that the sum of $2x$ and $7x$ is $9x$. Remind students that they found the same result when they combined like terms in the unit *Frogs, Fleas, and Painted Cubes*.

> What general rules have you discovered about the relationship between expressions in factored form and expressions in expanded form?

Students should offer a description of the distributive property using their own language. For example, if one of the dimensions of a rectangle is written as the sum $a + b$ and the other dimension is c, then the area is $c(a + b)$. Or, a and b can each be multiplied by c to find the area of the smaller rectangles and then those can be added to produce $ac + bc$.

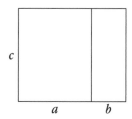

To lead into the next investigation, you might explain that this rule is called the *distributive property* and introduce the concept of distributing a factor over a sum or factoring out a common factor from a sum of terms:

$$a(b + c) = ab + ac$$

As a closing activity, you might have students make up their own pool problems and pose them to each other. Each student should draw a pool divided into sections, exchange drawings with a partner, and write two expressions for the area of the partner's pool.

Additional Answers

Answers to Problem 2.1 Follow-Up

1. The graphs and tables will be the same for all the equations (except for graph scales and specific table entries).

s	N
1	8
2	12
3	16
4	20
5	24
6	28
7	32
8	36
9	40

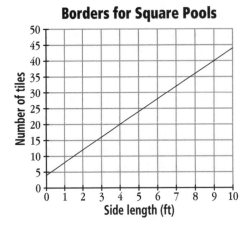

Borders for Square Pools

2. The relationship is linear; explanations will vary. For example, the table shows that as the side length of the pool increases by 1, the number of border tiles increases by 4; this pattern indicates a linear relationship. The graph is a straight line, so the relationship is linear. The equation $N = 4s + 4$ is a linear equation of the form $y = mx + b$.

Answers to Problem 2.2

Students' illustrations and ideas will vary; one possibility for each expression is shown here.

A. $4(s + 1)$

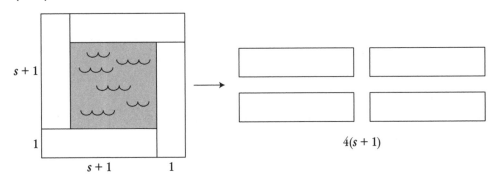

B. $s + s + s + s + 4$

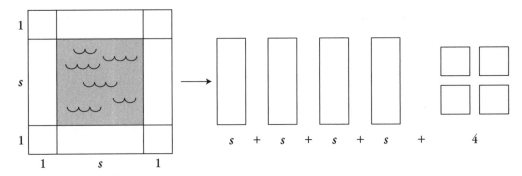

C. $2s + 2(s + 2)$

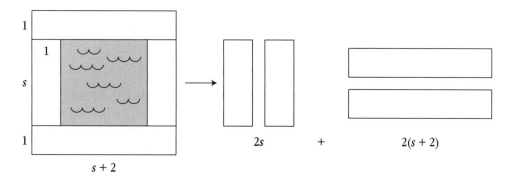

D. $4(s + 2) - 4$

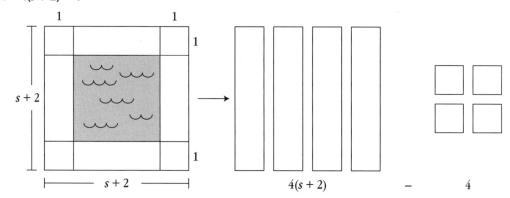

E.   Explanations will vary. Students may use geometric reasoning, tables, graphs, or symbol manipulation to explain their ideas about the equivalences.

Answers to Problem 2.2 Follow-Up

1.   The five expressions yield the same result for this value of s. It is possible that the expressions are all equivalent, but we can't conclude this from checking one value.

$4s + 4 = 4(10) + 4 = 44$
$4(s + 1) = 4(10 + 1) = 44$
$s + s + s + s + 4 = 10 + 10 + 10 + 10 + 4 = 44$
$2s + 2(s + 2) = 2(10) + 2(10 + 2) = 44$
$4(s + 2) - 4 = 4(10 + 2) - 4 = 44$

2.   The graphs and tables of the expressions are the same, which supports the idea that the expressions are equivalent.

s	N
1	8
2	12
3	16
4	20
5	24
6	28
7	32
8	36
9	40
10	44

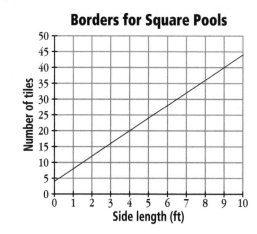

Borders for Square Pools

Answers to Problem 2.3 Follow-Up

1. a. Rectangles i, iii, and v have an area of $5(4 + x)$.

    b. $5(4) + 5(x)$ or $20 + 5x$

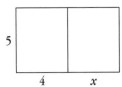

$$\text{area} = \text{length} \times \text{width}$$
$$= 5(4 + x)$$

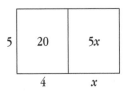

$$\text{area} = \text{area of left square} +$$
$$\text{area of right square}$$
$$= 20 + 5x$$

    c. Rectangle ii has an area of $5x + 4x$.

    d. $x(5 + 4)$

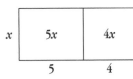

$$\text{area} = \text{area of left square} +$$
$$\text{area of right square}$$
$$= 5x + 4x$$

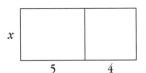

$$\text{area} = \text{length} \times \text{width}$$
$$= x(5 + 4)$$

2. a.

$\text{area} = 5x + 10$

$\text{area} = 5(x + 2)$

    b. Possible table:

x	$5x + 10$	$5(x + 2)$
1	$5 + 10 = 15$	$5(3) = 15$
6	$30 + 10 = 40$	$5(8) = 40$
13.5	$67.5 + 10 = 77.5$	$5(15.5) = 77.5$
20	$100 + 10 = 110$	$5(22) = 110$

The graphs of the equations $y = 5x + 10$ and $y = 5(x + 2)$ are the same.

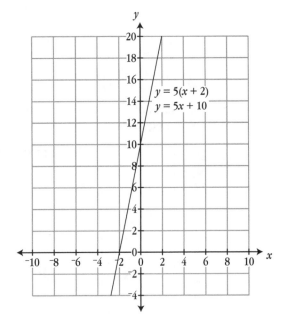

ACE Answers

Applications

Note: Possible answers are given for 13–18. Students might draw area models to demonstrate equivalence. In addition, equivalent expressions will have the same tables and graphs.

13. The expressions are equivalent because the terms $2x$ and $11x$ can be added to give $13x$.

14. The expressions are not equivalent because $x + 3.5x$ has an x added to the term $3.5x$.

15. The expressions are not equivalent because $5(x + 12)$ is equivalent to $5x + 60$, not equal to $5x + 12$.

16. The expressions are equivalent because the terms $6x$ and x can be added to give $7x$.

17. The expressions are equivalent because $2(1 + L + 5)$ is equivalent to $2(L + 6)$, which is equivalent to $2L + 12$.

18. The expressions are equivalent because the terms $3R$ and $5R$ can be added to give $8R$.

Mathematical Reflections

1. Saying that $4n + 4$ and $4(n + 1)$ are equivalent means that they may be symbolic representations for the same situation. For all values of n, they should give the same result. The diagram shows that they are equivalent by relating them to the areas of rectangles.

area $= 4n + 4$

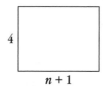

area $= 4(n + 1)$

In the table, the entries in the columns for $4n + 4$ and $4(n + 1)$ are identical, and when the related equations are graphed, there is only one line. These two expressions seem to produce the same pairs of values.

n	$4n + 4$	$4(n + 1)$
0	4	4
1	8	8
2	12	12
3	16	16
4	20	20

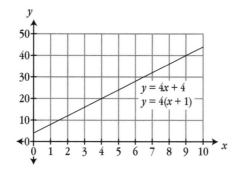

3. Note: Explanations will vary. One possibility is given for each part.

3a. The diagram shows that the expressions 5(2x) and 2x(5) represent the same rectangle.

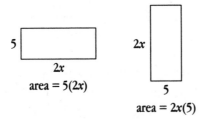

area = 5(2x)

area = 2x(5)

3b. Substituting values of x gives the same results.

x	5 + 2x	2x + 5
1	5 + 2(1) = 7	2(1) + 5 = 7
3	5 + 2(3) = 11	2(3) + 5 = 11
6	5 + 2(6) = 17	2(6) + 5 = 17

3c. The diagram on the left shows that 5(10) + 2 and 50 + 2 both equal 52; the diagram on the right shows that 5(10 + 2) equals 60.

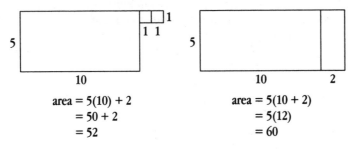

area = 5(10) + 2
= 50 + 2
= 52

area = 5(10 + 2)
= 5(12)
= 60

Some Important Properties

Students now acquire formal vocabulary for describing their experiences in the previous investigation, learning the names of the distributive property and the commutative properties. This is a significant moment in students' development of algebraic skills. If students memorize such properties without understanding why they work, they will be able to apply the "patterns" to obvious examples, but will have no power to recognize the patterns in varied forms and situations.

In Problem 3.1, Walking Together, students find two expressions for the money raised in a walkathon. They apply the distributive and commutative properties to show that the expressions are equivalent. In Problem 3.2, Estimating Profit, students find equivalent expressions for profit as income minus expenses. The context introduces distributing a negative sign to terms in parentheses. In Problem 3.3, Finding the Area of a Trapezoid, students work with greater symbolic complexity as they express the area of a trapezoid in different symbolic forms. They must show that the expressions are equivalent using the properties of real numbers while keeping in mind the underlying conceptualization each method represents. In Problem 3.4, Writing Quadratic Expressions, they investigate a situation involving equivalent quadratic expressions and consider the multiplication of binomials, both as an application of the distributive property and as an equivalence of areas.

Throughout the investigation, students apply the properties of real numbers to write equivalent expressions as they connect symbolic expressions with real-world contexts.

Mathematical and Problem-Solving Goals

- **To determine the impact of a negative quantity as a factor**

- **To use the distributive and commutative properties to show equivalence of expressions**

- **To use contextual clues to interpret symbolic expressions**

- **To solve a variety of problems using the distributive and commutative properties**

Materials		
Problem	For students	For the teacher
All	Graphing calculators	Transparencies: 3.1A to 3.4B (optional), overhead graphing calculator (optional)
3.3	Trapezoids cut from Labsheet 3.3 (optional), large sheets of paper (optional)	Transparency of Labsheet 3.3 (optional)
3.4	Large sheets of paper or blank transparencies (optional)	

Some Important Properties

In the last investigation, you used areas of rectangles to help you find equivalent expressions. The rectangle below, for example, illustrates that $4(5 + x) = 20 + 4x$.

```
      ┌──────────┬──────┐
    4 │          │      │
      └──────────┴──────┘
           5        x
```

This example illustrates an important property of the real number system called the **distributive property**. You can use the distributive property in two ways:

1. If an expression is written as a factor multiplied by a sum, you can use the distributive property to *multiply* the factor by each term in the sum.

$$4(5 + x) = 4(5) + 4x = 20 + 4x$$

2. If an expression is written as a sum of terms and the terms have a common factor, you can use the distributive property to rewrite the expression as the common factor multiplied by a sum. This process is called *factoring*.

$$20 + 4x = 4(5) + 4x = 4(5 + x)$$

The diagram below illustrates the two ways of applying the distributive property.

multiply

$$r(s + t) = rs + rt$$

factor

Think about this!

Brenda says that because subtracting a number is the same as adding its opposite, you can use the distributive property to rewrite expressions involving differences. She gave this example:

$$5(x - 2) = 5(x + {}^{-}2)$$
$$= 5(x) + 5({}^{-}2)$$
$$= 5x + {}^{-}10$$
$$= 5x - 10$$

Can you explain each step in Brenda's example?

The equations $2x + 10 = 10 + 2x$ and $2(x + 5) = (x + 5)2$ illustrate two other important properties. The **commutative property of addition** says that the order in which two quantities are added does not matter. The **commutative property of multiplication** says that the order in which two quantities are multiplied does not matter. These properties can be written using symbols as

$$a + b = b + a \quad \text{and} \quad ab = ba.$$

These properties are sometimes called the **rearrangement property of addition** and the **rearrangement property of multiplication**.

The distributive and commutative properties are useful for writing equivalent expressions. The distributive property allows you to rewrite expressions that involve combinations of multiplication and addition or subtraction. The commutative properties allow you to reorder the terms in an expression so you can group like terms. In this investigation, you will use these properties to solve some interesting problems.

Walking Together

Grouping:
pairs

Launch

- Review the factored and expanded forms of expressions.

- Introduce the distributive property.

- Talk about the walkathon and about writing expressions for the amount to be raised.

- Have pairs work on the problem.

Explore

- Assign the follow-up to pairs or as homework.

Summarize

- Have students share their equations and what they have learned about showing the equivalence of expressions.

- Review the follow-up.

Assignment Choices

ACE questions 2, 4, 11, 12, 19–21, 38, 48–51, and unassigned choices from earlier problems

---

3.1 Walking Together

Leanne, Gilberto, and Alana are participating in a walkathon to raise money for a local hospital. Each participant must find sponsors to pledge a certain amount of money per mile walked.

- Leanne asks her sponsors to pledge $1 for each mile she walks.
- Gilberto asks his sponsors to pledge $2 for each mile he walks.
- Alana asks her sponsors to pledge $5 plus $0.50 for each mile she walks.

The amount raised by each student will depend on the number of sponsors the student has and the number of miles the student walks.

Problem 3.1

The walkathon organizers have offered a prize to the three-person team that raises the most money. Leanne, Gilberto, and Alana will walk together and combine their earnings to compete for the prize. On the day of the walkathon, Leanne has pledges from 16 sponsors, Gilberto has pledges from 7 sponsors, and Alana has pledges from 11 sponsors.

A. For each student, write an equation for the amount of money the student will raise if he or she walks x miles. Then write an equation for the total amount the three-person team will raise if they walk x miles.

A_{Leanne} = _____

A_{Gilberto} = _____

A_{Alana} = _____

A_{total} = _____

B. Alana asked each of her 11 sponsors to pledge $5 in addition to an amount per mile, so the team will raise $55 regardless of how far they walk.

1. Excluding the $55, how much will the team raise per mile?

2. Use your answer from part 1 to help you write a different equation for the total amount the team will raise if they walk x miles.

C. 1. Use the distributive and commutative properties to show that the two expressions you wrote for the total amount the team will raise are equivalent.

2. Verify that the expressions are equivalent by making and comparing tables or graphs.

Say It with Symbols

Answers to Problem 3.1

A. $A_{\text{Leanne}} = 16x$

$A_{\text{Gilberto}} = 7(2x)$

$A_{\text{Alana}} = 11(5 + 0.5x)$

$A_{\text{total}} = 16x + 7(2x) + 11(5 + 0.5x)$ (or some similar form)

B. **1.** Leanne will raise $1 per mile for each of her 16 sponsors, for a total of $16 per mile. Gilberto will raise $2 per mile for each of his 7 sponsors, for a total of $14 per mile. Alana will raise $0.50 per mile for each of her 11 sponsors, for a total of $5.50 per mile. So, the team will raise 16 + 14 + 5.50 = $35.50 per mile.

2. $A_{\text{total}} = 35.5x + 55$

C. See page 52m.

Investigation 3

3.2

Estimating Profit

Problem 3.1 Follow-Up

In Problem 3.1, you used the distributive and commutative properties to write equivalent expressions for the amount of money the team will raise. The context of the problem may have helped you understand why these properties make sense. Now you will practice applying the properties to algebraic expressions that are not in context.

In 1–12, tell whether the expressions are equivalent, and explain your reasoning.

1. $3x + 5x$ and $8x$
2. $3x + 5$ and $8x$
3. $4(x + 7)$ and $4x + 7$
4. $5(x + 2)$ and $5x + 10$
5. $12 + 8x$ and $4(3 + 2x)$
6. $4x + x + 2x$ and $8x$
7. $7 + 5x$ and $5x + 7$
8. $3x + 8$ and $8x + 3$
9. $5x + 3x + 4x$ and $4x + 5x + 3x$
10. $6 + 2t$ and $2(t + 3)$
11. $2(L + 2) + 2W$ and $2L + 2W + 4$
12. $2L + 2W + 4$ and $2(L + W + 2)$

3.2 Estimating Profit

At their planning meeting, the organizers of the hospital walkathon discussed expenses and income. They made the following estimates:

- Expense for posters and newspaper, radio, and TV ads: $500
- Expense for souvenir T-shirts for participants: $6 per child, $8.50 per adult
- Income from business sponsors whose logos will appear on T-shirts and signs: $1000
- Expense for paramedics and an ambulance in case of emergency: $250
- Income from registration fees: $5 per child, $15 per adult

Notice that some of the expenses are fixed, while others depend on the number of adults and children who participate. The difference between the total income and the total expenses is the profit. The organizers will donate any profit from the event to the hospital.

Launch

- Talk about the expenses and income for the walkathon.
- Have students work on the problem individually or in pairs.

Explore

- Help students understand the distribution of the negative sign by relating it to the context.

Summarize

- Discuss how to check expressions for equivalence.
- Help students generalize the rule for distributing a minus sign.
- Assign and then review the follow-up.

Answers to Problem 3.1 Follow-Up

Explanations will vary. One way of reasoning is given for each problem.

1. equivalent; $3x + 5x = (3 + 5)x = 8x$
2. not equivalent; The related equations, $y = 3x + 5$ and $y = 8x$, have different slopes.
3. not equivalent; $4(x + 7) = 4x + 28 \neq 4x + 7$
4. equivalent; $5(x + 2) = 5x + 5(2) = 5x + 10$
5. equivalent; $12 + 8x = 4(3) + 4(2x) = 4(3 + 2x)$
6. not equivalent; $4x + x + 2x = (4 + 1 + 2)x = 7x \neq 8x$
7. equivalent; $7 + 5x = 5x + 7$ because the order in which numbers are added does not matter.
8–12. See page 52n.

Assignment Choices

ACE questions 1, 3, 5–10, 25–29, 46, 47, and unassigned choices from earlier problems

Problem 3.2

A. Estimate the total income, the total expenses, and the total profit if 40 children and 30 adults participate in the walkathon.

B. Write two equivalent expressions for the total income in terms of the number of adults, *a*, and the number of children, *c*, who participate.

C. Write two equivalent expressions for the total expenses in terms of the number of adults, *a*, and the number of children, *c*, who participate.

D. Use parentheses and your results from parts B and C to write an expression showing the profit as total income minus total expenses. That is, express the profit as (expression for income) – (expression for expenses).

E. Write an expression for profit that is equivalent to your expression from part D but that is as short as possible. Use the distributive and commutative properties to show that the two profit expressions are equivalent.

F. Evaluate your profit expressions from parts D and E for *a* = 100 and *c* = 75. Can you conclude from your results that the expressions are equivalent? Explain.

G. Compare the profit expressions you wrote in parts D and E. What are the advantages and disadvantages of writing the profit expression in a shorter form?

■ **Problem 3.2 Follow-Up**

In Problem 3.2, you might have written this expression for profit:

$$(1000 + 5c + 15a) - (500 + 6c + 8.50a + 250)$$

The first pair of parentheses in this expression can be deleted, but to remove the second pair, you must *distribute* the minus sign to each term within the parentheses.

$$(1000 + 5c + 15a) - (500 + 6c + 8.50a + 250) = 1000 + 5c + 15a - 500 - 6c - 8.50a - 250$$

Distributing the minus sign to each term is a special case of the distributive property.

$$^-(s + t) = {}^-1(s + t) = {}^-1(s) + {}^-1(t) = {}^-s + {}^-t = {}^-s - t$$

Answers to Problem 3.2

A. Income will be 1000 + 5(40) + 15(30) = $1650. Expenses will be 500 + 250 + 6(40) + 8.50(30) = $1245. The profit is thus $1650 – $1245 = $405.

Note: In B–G, students may write and use many expressions. Some examples are given.

B. 1000 + 5*c* + 15*a*, or 1000 + 5(*c* + 3*a*)

C. 500 + 250 + 6*c* + 8.50*a*, or 750 + 6*c* + 8.50*a*

D. (1000 + 5*c* + 15*a*) – (750 + 6*c* + 8.50*a*)

E. Answers will vary; students may find their expression by reasoning about the situation or applying the properties. Possible answer: 250 – *c* + 6.50*a*; Demonstration of equivalence: (1000 + 5*c* + 15*a*) – (750 + 6*c* + 8.50*a*) = 1000 + 5*c* + 15*a* – 750 – 6*c* – 8.50*a* = (1000 – 750) + (5*c* – 6*c*) + (15*a* – 8.50*a*) = 250 – *c* + 6.50*a*

F, G. See page 52n.

1. Benjamin's math test consisted of 10 questions, each worth 5 points. Benjamin answered two questions incorrectly. Show at least two ways to calculate his score.

2. **a.** Describe a situation that can be represented by the expression $100 - (x + y)$. Explain what x and y represent in your situation.
   b. Use the distributive property to help you write an expression that is equivalent to $100 - (x + y)$.

3. **a.** Describe a situation that can be represented by the expression $50 - 2x - 2y$. Explain what x and y represent in your situation.
   b. Use the distributive property to help you write an expression that is equivalent to $50 - 2x - 2y$.

4. The expression $3 + 2x$ is equivalent to $2x + 3$. Is $3 - 2x$ equivalent to $2x - 3$? Explain why or why not.

5. Apply the properties you have learned in this investigation to simplify each expression.
   a. $(9x + 15) - (8 + 2x)$
   b. $(7x - 12) - (9x + 15)$
   c. $(14r + 9t + 15) + (23 - 9r + 3t)$
   d. $19 - 12x + 20 + 9x$

3.3 Finding the Area of a Trapezoid

The figure below is a trapezoid. A *trapezoid* is a quadrilateral with one pair of parallel sides. The parallel sides, labeled a and b, are called the *bases* of the trapezoid. The distance from side a to side b, labeled b, is the *height*.

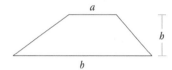

Ms. Ochoa's students have learned how to find areas of triangles, rectangles, and parallelograms. Now, Ms. Ochoa has challenged her students to find a method for calculating the area of a trapezoid.

Tua, Sam, and Carlos have found three methods for calculating the area. Each method involves dividing and rearranging the trapezoid into other shapes.

Investigation 3: Some Important Properties 39

Answers to Problem 3.2 Follow-Up

1. Possible answer: $10(5) - 2(5)$, $(10 - 2)5$, $10(5) - 5 - 5$, $50 - (5 + 5)$

2. **a.** Possible answers: $100 - (x + y)$ represents the balance in a checking account that began with $100 and had two withdrawals, one for x dollars and one for y dollars. Or, on a 100-point test, two questions, one worth x points and one worth y points, were answered incorrectly.
   b. $100 - (x + y) = 100 - x - y$

3. **a.** Possible answer: $50 - 2x - 2y$ represents a student's score on a 50-point test; four questions were answered incorrectly, two worth x points and two worth y points.
   b. $50 - 2x - 2y = 50 + 2(^-x - y)$, or $50 - 2(x + y)$

4, 5. See page 52n.

3.3

Finding the Area of a Trapezoid

At a Glance

Grouping: *individuals, then small groups*

Launch

- Review area formulas for polygons.
- Use an example to introduce the problem.
- Have individuals begin work, then finish the problem and do the follow-up in groups of two or three.

Explore

- Make paper trapezoids available to students who want to use them.
- Ask students who finish early to invent their own methods.

Summarize

- Have students share their reasoning for each method.
- Discuss the follow-up.
- Offer another expression to assess students' understanding.

Assignment Choices

ACE questions 13–18, 22–24, 39–42, 52–57, and unassigned choices from earlier problems

Investigation 3 39

Problem 3.3

The students made drawings to illustrate their methods for calculating the area of a trapezoid. Try to figure out how each student thought about the problem.

Tua's method

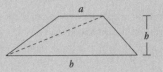

Sam's method

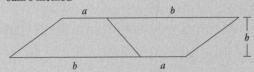

Carlos's method

A. Explain each student's method for finding the area.

B. Write an algebraic expression to describe each method.

C. Show that the expressions you wrote in part B are equivalent.

■ Problem 3.3 Follow-Up

1. a. Natasha lost her drawing, but she had written this expression for finding the area of a trapezoid:

$$\tfrac{1}{2}b(b-a) + ba$$

Use this expression to decide what Natasha's drawing might have looked like. Make a drawing, and use it to help explain Natasha's method for finding the area.

b. Is Natasha's expression equivalent to the three expressions in part B? Explain.

2. A trapezoid has a height of 10 centimeters and bases of 9 centimeters and 15 centimeters. Find the area of the trapezoid using each of the four expressions.

Answers to Problem 3.3

A. Tua divided the trapezoid into two triangles, one with base *a* and one with base *b* and each with a height of *h*; the area of the trapezoid is equal to the sum of the areas of the triangles. Sam added an identical trapezoid to make a parallelogram with base *a* + *b* and height *h*; the area of the parallelogram is (*a* + *b*)*h*, which is *double* the area of the trapezoid. Carlos cut the trapezoid horizontally and rearranged the pieces to make a parallelogram with base *b* + *a* and height $\tfrac{1}{2}h$.

B. Tua's method: $\tfrac{1}{2}ah + \tfrac{1}{2}bh$ Sam's method: $\frac{(b+a)h}{2}$ Carlos's method: $(b + a)(\tfrac{1}{2}h)$

C. Students might show that each expression is equivalent to $\tfrac{1}{2}h(a + b)$:

$\tfrac{1}{2}ah + \tfrac{1}{2}bh = \tfrac{1}{2}h(a + b)$

$\frac{(b+a)h}{2} = \tfrac{1}{2}(b + a)h = \tfrac{1}{2}h(b + a) = \tfrac{1}{2}h(a + b)$

$(b + a)(\tfrac{h}{2}) = \tfrac{1}{2}h(b + a) = \tfrac{1}{2}h(a + b)$

3.4 Writing Quadratic Expressions

In your work in this unit, you have discovered that a situation can often be represented by different, but equivalent, algebraic expressions. Most of the expressions you have worked with have been linear expressions. In this problem, you will practice finding equivalent *quadratic* expressions.

The table below shows the results of the games played by a five-team soccer league. Each team played each of the other teams twice—once at home and once away. A *W* means the home team won the game; an *L* means the home team lost. For example, the Alligators won their home game against the Cats, but they lost when they played on the Cats' home field. What do the "—" symbols mean? How many games were played in all?

	Visiting Team				
	Alligators	Buzzards	Cats	Ducks	Elks
Alligators	—	W	W	L	W
Buzzards	L	—	L	L	W
Cats	W	W	—	L	L
Ducks	W	W	W	—	W
Elks	L	W	W	W	—

Home Team (label on left of table)

At a Glance

Grouping:
small groups

Launch

■ Quickly review quadratic relationships.

■ Talk about the table for the five-team league.

■ Have groups of two to four work on the problem and follow-up.

Explore

■ Distribute large sheets of paper or blank transparencies for students to record their methods. *(optional)*

Summarize

■ Have groups share all the expressions they found.

■ Review the follow-up questions.

Answers to Problem 3.3 Follow-Up

1. a. See page 52n.

   b. Natasha's expression is equivalent to the three other expressions because it is equivalent to $\frac{1}{2}h(a + b)$:

   $$\frac{1}{2}h(b - a) + ha = \frac{1}{2}hb - \frac{1}{2}ha + ha = \frac{1}{2}hb + \frac{1}{2}ha = h(\frac{1}{2})(b + a) = h(\frac{1}{2})(a + b)$$

2. Note: This is a good opportunity to review order of operations using each expression.

   $\frac{1}{2}ah + \frac{1}{2}bh = \frac{1}{2}(9)(10) + \frac{1}{2}(15)(10) = 45 + 75 = 120$ cm²

   $\frac{(b + a)h}{2} = \frac{(15 + 9)10}{2} = \frac{24(10)}{2} = \frac{240}{2} = 120$ cm²

   $(b + a)(\frac{1}{2}h) = (15 + 9)(\frac{1}{2})(10) = 24(5) = 120$ cm²

   $\frac{1}{2}h(b - a) + ha = \frac{1}{2}(10)(15 - 9) + 10(9) = 5(6) + 10(9) = 30 + 90 = 120$ cm²

Assignment Choices

ACE questions 30–37, 43–45, and unassigned choices from earlier problems

Assessment

It is appropriate to use the quiz after this problem.

Problem 3.4

In parts A–C, you will explore three ways of thinking about this question: If a league has n teams and each team plays each of the other teams twice, how many games are played in all?

A. Figure out how many games would be played for leagues with 2, 3, 4, 5, and 6 teams. Record your results in a table similar to the one below.

Number of teams	2	3	4	5	6
Number of games					

Look for a pattern in your table. Use the pattern to write an expression for the number of games played by a league with n teams.

B. Suppose a sports reporter wants to attend exactly one game in the schedule of an n-team league.

   1. How many choices does the reporter have for the home team for the game she attends?

   2. Once she has chosen a home team, how many choices does she have for the visiting team?

   3. Use your answers from parts 1 and 2 to write an expression for the total number of games the reporter can choose from.

C. Suppose you made a table similar to the one on page 41 to record wins and losses for an n-team league.

Visiting Team

	T_1	T_2	T_3	$\cdots$	T_n
T_1					
T_2					
T_3					
$\vdots$					
T_n					

Home Team

   1. How many cells would your table have?

   2. How many cells in the table would not be used for W or L entries?

   3. Use your answers from parts 1 and 2 to write an expression for the total number of games played.

D. In parts A–C, you wrote expressions for the number of games played by an n-team league. Show that these expressions are equivalent.

Answers to Problem 3.4

A. The pattern in the table can be expressed as $n(n) - n$, as $n^2 - n$, or as $n(n - 1)$.

Number of teams	2	3	4	5	6
Number of games	2	6	12	20	30

B. 1. n 2. $n - 1$ 3. $n(n - 1)$

C. 1. $n(n)$, or n^2 2. n 3. $n(n) - n$, or $n^2 - n$

D. $n(n) - n = n^2 - n = n(n) - n(1) = n(n - 1)$; Students might also point out that the expressions are related to the same table or that the reasoning behind each expression makes sense.

■ **Problem 3.4 Follow-Up**

Many quadratic expressions can be written in both factored form and expanded form. The area of the purple rectangle below can be written as $x^2 + 3x$ or as $x(x + 3)$.

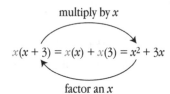

You can use the distributive property to show the equivalence of the factored and expanded forms of a quadratic expression. For example, you can change $x^2 + 3x$ to $x(x + 3)$ by factoring an x from each term. You can change $x(x + 3)$ to $x^2 + 3x$ by multiplying each term by x.

$$\text{multiply by } x$$
$$x(x + 3) = x(x) + x(3) = x^2 + 3x$$
$$\text{factor an } x$$

You can apply the distributive property to more complex factored expressions. This example shows how you can change the factored expression $(x + 2)(x + 3)$ to expanded form by applying the distributive property several times.

$$
\begin{aligned}
(x + 2)(x + 3) &= (x + 2)x + (x + 2)3 &&\text{Multiply } (x + 2) \text{ by each term of } x + 3.\\
&= x^2 + 2x + (x + 2)3 &&\text{Multiply } x \text{ by each term of } x + 2.\\
&= x^2 + 2x + 3x + 6 &&\text{Multiply } 3 \text{ by each term of } x + 2.\\
&= x^2 + 5x + 6 &&\text{Combine like terms.}
\end{aligned}
$$

Writing an expanded quadratic expression in factored form often poses more difficult challenges. You will learn more about factoring quadratic expressions in future math classes.

In 1–6, use the distributive property to find an expression that is equivalent to the given expression. Check each answer by using your calculator to compare tables and graphs.

1. $x(^{-}4x + 3)$ **2.** $(4x + 3)(x + 7)$ **3.** $(x - 4.5)(x + 6.5)$

4. $(2x - 5)(5x - 2)$ **5.** $x^2 - 6x$ **6.** $12x - 3x^2$

7. Look at your reasoning and your results from questions 1–6.
  a. Describe any general rules you discover for multiplying two linear factors.
  b. Describe any general rules you discover for factoring a quadratic expression.

Answers to Problem 3.4 Follow-Up

1. $x(^{-}4x + 3) = {}^{-}4x^2 + 3x$

2. $(4x + 3)(x + 7) = (4x + 3)x + (4x + 3)7 = 4x^2 + 3x + 28x + 21 = 4x^2 + 31x + 21$

3. $(x - 4.5)(x + 6.5) = (x - 4.5)x + (x - 4.5)6.5 = x^2 - 4.5x + 6.5x - 29.25 = x^2 - 2x - 29.25$

4. $(2x - 5)(5x - 2) = (2x - 5)5x - (2x - 5)2 = 10x^2 - 25x - (4x - 10) = 10x^2 - 25x - 4x + 10 = 10x^2 - 29x + 10$

5. $x^2 - 6x = x(x - 6)$

6. $12x - 3x^2 = 3x(4 - x)$

7. See page 52n.

Answers

Applications

Note: 1–3 reinforce the idea that equivalent expressions yield equal values when evaluated and that this fact can be used to check the equivalence of expressions.

1a. $3x - 4 - 2x$, or $x - 4$

1b. Each expression equals 1 when $x = 5$ and $^-5$ when $x = ^-1$.

2a. $3x + 6 + 2x + 4$, or $5x + 10$, or $5(x + 2)$

2b. Each expression equals 35 when $x = 5$ and 5 when $x = ^-1$.

3a. $(3 - 2)(x + 2)$, or $3x + 6 - 2x - 4$, or $x + 2$

3b. Each expression equals 7 when $x = 5$ and 1 when $x = ^-1$.

4–9. See below right.

10. See page 52o.

As you work on these ACE questions, use your calculator whenever you need it.

Applications

1. a. Write an expression that is equivalent to $3x - (4 + 2x)$.

  b. Evaluate $3x - (4 + 2x)$ and the expression you wrote for $x = 5$ and $x = ^-1$.

2. a. Write an expression that is equivalent to $3(x + 2) + 2(x + 2)$.

  b. Evaluate $3(x + 2) + 2(x + 2)$ and the expression you wrote for $x = 5$ and $x = ^-1$.

3. a. Write an expression that is equivalent to $3(x + 2) - 2(x + 2)$.

  b. Evaluate $3(x + 2) - 2(x + 2)$ and the expression you wrote for $x = 5$ and $x = ^-1$.

In 4–9, use the distributive and commutative properties to write two expressions that are equivalent to the given expression. Then tell which of the three expressions is easiest to evaluate for a given x value.

4. $3x + 2 + 5x$

5. $12 - 8x + 15 + 10x$

6. $(3x^2 + 5x + 8) + (9x^2 + 2x - 7)$

7. $(5 - 7x) - 2(5x + 12)$

8. $7(4x - 2) + 3(5 + 2x)$

9. $(3x^2 + 5x + 8) - (9x^2 + 2x - 7)$

10. a. Evaluate the expression $5000 - 50(75 - T)$ for $T = 25$. Describe the order in which you performed the operations.

  b. Write an expression that is equivalent to $5000 - 50(75 - T)$, and evaluate your expression for $T = 25$. Did the order in which you performed the operations change? Explain.

  c. Which expression is easier to evaluate?

Note: In 4–9, a possible answer is given. The questions offer practice in manipulating expressions and encourage working toward a simpler form, though the focus is not on finding the "simplest" form. Some of the expressions require flexible combinations of the properties. For these problems in particular, ask students to justify their results, but don't overemphasize simplification.

4. $(3 + 5)x + 2$ and $8x + 2$; The last expression is the easiest to use.

5. $27 - 8x + 10x$ and $27 + 2x$; The last expression is the easiest to use.

6. $(3x^2 + 9x^2) + (5x + 2x) + (8 - 7)$ and $12x^2 + 7x + 1$; The last expression is the easiest to use.

7. $5 - 7x - 10x - 24$ and $^-19 - 17x$; The last expression is the easiest to use.

8. $28x - 14 + 15 + 6x$ and $34x + 1$; The last expression is the easiest to use.

9. $3x^2 + 5x + 8 - 9x^2 - 2x + 7$ and $^-6x^2 + 3x + 15$; The last expression is the easiest to use.

11. Describe a real-life situation you could use to convince someone that $2x + 5x$ and $7x$ are different ways of expressing the same information.

12. Describe a real-life situation you could use to convince someone that $3x + 5 + 4x$ and $7x + 5$ are different ways of expressing the same information.

In 13–18, copy the statement and insert parentheses, if needed, to make the statement true. For example, to make $3x + 1 - 2x = x + 3$ a true statement, you could write $3(x + 1) - 2x = x + 3$.

13. $6x - 4x - 3x = 5x$

14. $6x - 4x - 3x = {}^{-}x$

15. $7 + 5p - p = 11p$

16. $7 + 5p - p = 7$

17. $7 + 5p - p = 7 + 4p$

18. $7 + 5p - p = 0$

In 19 and 20, copy the statement, replacing the question mark with a number or an expression that makes the statement true.

19. $2(4 + ?) = 18$

20. $2(4 + ?) = 8 + 6x$

21. **a.** Write 12 as a product of two factors and as a product of three factors.

b. Write 12 as a sum of two terms and as a sum of three terms.

c. Write 12 as a product of two factors in which one of the factors is the sum of two terms.

Investigation 3: Some Important Properties 45

---

11. Possible answer: Joy and Noah are organizing a bike race. They will charge $2 per student to enter the race and $5 per student for meals. Joy collects the entry fees and Noah collects the meal fees. For x students, Joy should collect $2x$ dollars and Noah should collect $5x$ dollars, a total of $2x + 5x$ dollars. Since each student who enters will pay 7 dollars, the total amount collected will be $7x$ dollars.

12. Answers will vary. The story from question 11 could be adapted, with a $3 entry fee, a $4 charge for meals, and an anonymous donation of $5.

13. $6x - (4x - 3x) = 5x$

14. Parentheses are not needed.

15. $(7 + 5)p - p = 11p$

16. $7 + 5(p - p) = 7$

17. Parentheses are not needed.

18. $(7 + 5)(p - p) = 0$

19. $2(4 + 5) = 18$

20. $2(4 + 3x) = 8 + 6x$

21. Answers will vary. Some possibilities are given here.

21a. $12 = 2(6) = 3(4) = 12(1) = 10(1.2)$ and $12 = 2(2)(3) = 2(5)(1.2) = 1(2)(6)$

21b. $12 = 5 + 7 = 6 + 6 = 10.5 + 1.5$ and $12 = 2 + 6 + 4 = 9 + 2 + 1$

21c. $12 = 2(3 + 3) = 4(1 + 2) = 10(1 + 0.2)$

Connections

22. factored form: $x(x + 3)$, expanded form: $x^2 + 3x$; The equivalence $x(x + 3) = x^2 + 3x$ illustrates the distributive property because x is multiplied by each term in the sum $x + 3$ or factored from each term in $x^2 + 3x$.

23. factored form: $(x + 3)(x + 5)$, expanded form: $x^2 + 8x + 15$; The equivalence $(x + 3)(x + 5) = x^2 + 8x + 15$ illustrates the distributive property because the factor $x + 3$ is multiplied by each term in $x + 5$, and then each term in $x + 3$ is multiplied by x and also by 5: $(x + 3)(x + 5) = (x + 3)x + (x + 3)5 = x^2 + 3x + 5x + 15 = x^2 + 8x + 15$.

24. factored form: $(x + x)(x + 5)$, expanded form: $2x^2 + 10x$; The equivalence $(x + x)(x + 5) = 2x^2 + 10x$ illustrates the distributive property because, after $x + x$ is simplified to $2x$, this term is multiplied by each term in the factor $x + 5$: $2x(x + 5) = 2x^2 + 10x$.

25. See below right.

26, 27. See page 52o.

28, 29. See page 52p.

Connections

In 22–24, write two expressions, one in factored form and one in expanded form, for the area of the purple rectangle. Show how the equivalence of the two expressions illustrates the distributive property.

22.

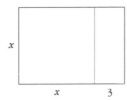

23.

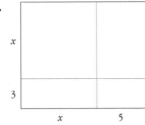

24.

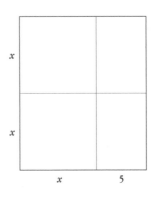

In 25–29, do parts a–c.

25. $^-3x + 6 + 5x$ and $6 + 2x$ **26.** $10 - 5x$ and $5x - 10$

27. $(3x + 4) + (2x - 3)$ and $5x + 1$ **28.** $9x - 5(x - 3) - 20$ and $5 - 4x$

29. $(10x - 5) - (4x + 2)$ and $10x - 5 - 4x + 2$

    a. Make a table and a graph for the two expressions. Show x values from $^-5$ to 5 on the graph.

    b. Based on your table and graph, tell whether you think the expressions are equivalent.

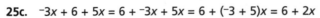

25a.

x	$^-3x + 6 + 5x$	$6 + 2x$
$^-3$	0	0
$^-2$	2	2
$^-1$	4	4
0	6	6
1	8	8
2	10	10
3	12	12

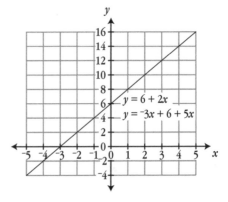

25b. The expressions are equivalent because the table values are the same and the graph is a single line.

25c. $^-3x + 6 + 5x = 6 + ^-3x + 5x = 6 + (^-3 + 5)x = 6 + 2x$

   c. If you think the expressions are equivalent, use the commutative and distributive properties to verify their equivalence. If you think they are not equivalent, use the properties to show why.

In 30–32, use the distributive property to show that the expressions are equivalent. Draw a rectangle to illustrate their equivalence.

30. $x(x + 5)$ and $x^2 + 5x$

31. $(2 + x)(2 + 3x)$ and $4 + 8x + 3x^2$

32. $(x + 2)(2x + 3)$ and $2x^2 + 7x + 6$

33. You have seen that many quadratic expressions can be written in factored form and in expanded form.

   a. Which form would you use to determine whether a quadratic relationship has a maximum point or a minimum point? Why?

   b. Which form would you use to find the x- and y-intercepts of a quadratic relationship? Why?

   c. Which form would you use to find the line of symmetry for a quadratic relationship? Why?

   d. Which form would you use to find the coordinates of the maximum or minimum point for a quadratic relationship? Why?

34. For each pair of expressions in questions 30–32, there is an associated quadratic relationship. For example, the expressions in question 30 are associated with the relationship $y = x(x + 5)$, or $y = x^2 + 5x$. Do parts a–c for each pair of expressions in questions 30–32.

   a. Find the x- and y-intercepts of the associated quadratic relationship.

   b. Find the line of symmetry.

   c. Find the coordinates of the maximum or minimum point.

   d. Sketch the graph and indicate the information from parts a–c.

Investigation 3: Some Important Properties **47**

---

30. $x(x + 5) = x(x) + 5(x) =$ $x^2 + 5x$

x	x^2	$5x$
	x	5

31, 32. See below left.

33, 34. See page 52p.

---

31. $(2 + x)(2 + 3x) = (2 + x)2 + (2 + x)3x$
$= 4 + 2x + 6x + 3x^2 = 4 + 8x + 3x^2$

2	4	6x
x	2x	3x²
	2	3x

32. $(x + 2)(2x + 3) = (x + 2)2x + (x + 2)3$
$= 2x^2 + 4x + 3x + 6 = 2x^2 + 7x + 6$

x	2x²	3x
2	4x	6
	2x	3

35. $5x^2 + x = x(5x) + x(1)$ $= x(5x + 1)$; They are equivalent.

36. $3x^2 + 15x = 3x(x + 5)$, which is not equivalent to $3x(x + 15)$. When $x = 0$, the value of $3x^2 + 15$ is 15, while the value of $3x^2 + 15x$ is 0.

37. $^-4x + 12x^2 = ^-4(x - 3x^2)$ $= ^-4x(1 - 3x)$; They are equivalent.

38a. Subtract 70 from the predicted high temperature, multiply that difference by 50, and add the resulting product to 200.

38b. Possible answers:
$V = 200 + 50T - 50(70)$,
$V = 200 + 50T - 3500$,
$V = 50T - 3300$,
$V = 50(T - 66)$

38c. For each increase of 1°F, the number of visitors increases by 50.

38d. $V = 200 + 50(83 - 70)$ $= 200 + 50(13) = 200 + 650$ $= 850$ visitors

38e, f. See below right.

In 35–37, tell whether the expressions are equivalent. If they are, use the distributive and commutative properties to illustrate their equivalence. If they are not equivalent, explain why not.

35. $5x^2 + x$ and $x(5x + 1)$

36. $3x^2 + 15$ and $3x(x + 15)$

37. $^-4x + 12x^2$ and $^-4x(1 - 3x)$

38. Data from past seasons show that the number of people who visit Water Works park on a given day depends on the day's high temperature. The manager wrote the equation $V = 200 + 50(T - 70)$ to estimate the number of visitors based on the day's predicted high temperature, T, in degrees Fahrenheit.

a. What sequence of operations do you need to perform to find the expected number of visitors for a given temperature?

b. Use the commutative and distributive properties to find a different equation for the number of visitors as a function of the temperature.

c. Describe how the expected number of visitors changes as the temperature increases.

d. Without using the table feature of your calculator, estimate the number of visitors on a day when the predicted high temperature is 83°F.

e. Estimate the number of visitors on a day when the predicted high temperature is 68°F and on a day when the predicted high temperature is 65°F. What do your answers indicate about the limitations of this equation model?

f. In parts c–e, which equation did you use to calculate your answers? Explain why you chose this equation.

38e. If the high temperature is 68°F,

$V = 200 + 50(68 - 70)$
$= 200 + 50(^-2)$
$= 200 - 100$
$= 100$ visitors

If the high temperature is 65°F,

$V = 200 + 50(65 - 70)$
$= 200 + 50(^-5)$
$= 200 - 250$
$= ^-50$ visitors

The model does not make sense for temperatures below 66°F. Zero visitors are predicted when $T = 66°F$.

38f. Answers will vary. Some students will use the "simplest" version because it is the easiest to use; some will use the original equation because is more helpful to keep track of what expressions mean, as when looking at the limitations of the model for predicting the number of visitors.

39. Suppose D dollars are invested in a money-market account that earns 10% interest per year. If no money is withdrawn, the amount of money in the account at the end of one year is $D + 0.10D$.

   a. Write an equivalent expression in factored form.

   b. If $1500 is invested, how much money will be in the account at the end of the first year?

40. a. Write an expression for the total price of an item that costs P dollars plus 6% sales tax.

   b. What is the total price of a jacket that costs $47 plus 6% sales tax?

41. a. A store is offering a 30% discount on all purchases. Write an expression for the discounted price of an item that normally sells for P dollars.

   b. What is the discounted price of a pair of hiking boots that normally sells for $68.50?

42. A tour operator's total expense for a bus tour with N people is $200 + 10N$. The tour operator charges each person $30.

   a. Write two equivalent expressions for the profit the tour operator will earn if N people go on the tour.

   b. What will the profit be if 10 people go on the tour? If 75 people go?

   c. How many people must go on the tour for the tour operator to break even? Explain.

   d. Write an expression for the average per-person profit the operator will earn.

39a. $D(1 + 0.10)$

39b. $1500(1.1) = 1650$

40a. $P + 0.06P$, or $P(1 + 0.06)$, or $1.06P$

40b. $1.06(47) = 49.82$

41a. $P - 0.30P$, or $P(1 - 0.30)$, or $0.70P$

41b. $0.70(68.50) = 47.95$

42a. Possible answers (recalling that profit = income − expenses): $30N - (200 + 10N)$, or $30N - 200 - 10N$, or $20N - 200$

42b. For 10 people, the profit is $20(10) - 200 = 0$. For 75 people, the profit is $20(75) - 200 = 1300$.

42c. The break-even point is 10 people; at that point, income and expenses are equal. (Note: Students will reason about this in a variety of ways. Investigation 4 emphasizes a systematic approach to such problems.)

42d. average profit per person $= \frac{20N - 200}{N}$

Extensions

43. $(x + 1)(x + 4) = (x + 4)x$ $+ (x + 4)1 = x^2 + 4x + x + 4$ $= x^2 + 5x + 4$; They are equivalent.

44. $3x(x + 15) = 3x^2 + 45x$ $\neq 3x^2 + 15x$

45. $(x - 5)(x + 2) = (x - 5)x$ $+ (x - 5)2 = x^2 - 5x + 2x - 10$ $= x^2 - 3x - 10$; They are equivalent.

46. When evaluating the second set of parentheses, Marcel distributed the minus sign to the 500 but not to the other three terms.

47. Kirtee combined $5c - 6c$ and found c instead of ^-c.

Note: In 48–51, the goal is to communicate the idea that equivalent forms might be helpful in doing mental computations.

48. $7(25) + 7(75) =$ $7(25 + 75) = 7(100) = 700$

49. $9(4) + 11(4) =$ $(9 + 11)4 = 20(4) = 80$

50. $3(99) + 3(101) =$ $3(99 + 101) = 3(200) = 600$

51. $5(106) = 5(100 + 6) =$ $5(100) + 5(6) = 500 + 30 =$ 530

Extensions

In 43–45, tell whether the expressions are equivalent. If they are, use the distributive and commutative properties to illustrate their equivalence.

43. $x^2 + 5x + 4$ and $(x + 1)(x + 4)$

44. $3x^2 + 15x$ and $3x(x + 15)$

45. $(x - 5)(x + 2)$ and $x^2 - 3x - 10$

In 46 and 47, use this information: In Problem 3.2, you may have written the following expression for the estimated profit from the walkathon:

$$(1000 + 5c + 15a) - (500 + 6c + 8.50a + 250)$$

An equivalent expression in simplified form is this:

$$250 - c + 6.50a$$

46. When Marcel simplified the profit expression, he found a different result. Study the steps in his reasoning, and find his mistake.

$$(1000 + 5c + 15a) - (500 + 6c + 8.50a + 250)$$
$$= 1000 + 5c + 15a - 500 + 6c + 8.50a + 250$$
$$= 1000 - 500 + 250 + 5c + 6c + 15a + 8.50a$$
$$= 750 + 11c + 23.50a$$

47. Kirtee found a different simplified expression. Study the steps in her reasoning, and find her mistake.

$$(1000 + 5c + 15a) - (500 + 6c + 8.50a + 250)$$
$$= 1000 + 5c + 15a - 500 - 6c - 8.50a - 250$$
$$= 1000 - 500 - 250 + 5c - 6c + 15a - 8.50a$$
$$= 250 + c + 6.50a$$

In 48–51, rewrite the expression so that the calculation is easy to do in your head. Then perform the calculation mentally, and check the result with your calculator.

48. $7(25) + 7(75)$

49. $9(4) + 11(4)$

50. $3(99) + 3(101)$

51. $5(106)$

In 52–57, use the distributive and commutative properties to simplify each expression as much as possible. Check that the original expression and your simplified expression are equivalent by testing several x values in both expressions.

52. $2(9x + 15) - (8 + 2x)$

53. $(7x - 12) - 2(3x + 10)$

54. $(19 - 12x) - (^-9x - 20)$

55. $2[3x + 5(x + 1)] - (10x + 2)$

56. $4 - 2(3x + 5) - (^-10 - 6x) - 4$

57. $(3x + 1)(2x - 3) - (1 - x)(1 - 6x)$

52. $2(9x + 15) - (8 + 2x) = 18x + 30 - 8 - 2x = 16x + 22$

53. $(7x - 12) - 2(3x + 10) = 7x - 12 - 6x - 20 = x - 32$

54. $(19 - 12x) - (^-9x - 20) = 19 - 12x + 9x + 20 = 39 - 3x$

55. $2[3x + 5(x + 1)] - (10x + 2) = 6x + 10(x + 1) - 10x - 2 = 6x + 10x + 10 - 10x - 2 = 6x + 8$

56. $4 - 2(3x + 5) - (^-10 - 6x) - 4 = 4 - 6x - 10 + 10 + 6x - 4 = 0$

57. $(3x + 1)(2x - 3) - (1 - x)(1 - 6x) = (3x + 1)2x - (3x + 1)3 - [(1 - x)1 - (1 - x)6x] =$
$6x^2 + 2x - 9x - 3 - (1 - x - 6x + 6x^2) = 6x^2 + 2x - 9x - 3 - 1 + x + 6x - 6x^2 = ^-4$

1. The distributive property can be used to rewrite expressions as the product of two or more factors (the factored form) or as the sum of two or more terms (the expanded form). The expression $2x(x + 5)$ can be written as the sum of two terms using the distributive property: $2x^2 + 10x$. The expression $6x^2 - 9x$ can be written in factored form using the distributive property: $3x(2x - 3)$. The commutative properties can be used to change the order of addition or multiplication. For example, $3x(2x - 3) = (2x - 3)3x$, $2x^2 + 10x = 10x + 2x^2$, and $3x - 8 + 6x - 4 - 5x + 6 = 3x + 6x - 5x + 6 - 4 - 8$.

2a. The students in grades 6, 7, and 8 are planning to build booths for the school carnival. Each class at each grade level will need three sheets of plywood, which can be expressed as $3x + 3y + 3z$, where x represents the number of grade 6 classes, y represents the number of grade 7 classes, and z represents the number of grade 8 classes. The total number of sheets of plywood needed can also be expressed as $3(x + y + z)$.

2b. $3(x + y + z) = 3(x) + 3(y) + 3(z) = 3(x + y + z)$

Mathematical Reflections

In this investigation, you used the distributive and commutative properties to write equivalent expressions. These questions will help you summarize what you have learned:

1 Explain how the distributive and commutative properties can be used to write equivalent expressions. Use examples to illustrate your explanations.

2 **a.** Give an example of a real-life situation that can be represented by at least two equivalent expressions. Explain how each expression represents the situation.

b. Use the distributive and commutative properties to show that the expressions are equivalent.

Think about your answers to these questions, discuss your ideas with other students and your teacher, and then write a summary of your findings in your journal.

Tips for the Linguistically Diverse Classroom

Diagram Code The Diagram Code technique is described in detail in *Getting to Know Connected Mathematics*. Students use a minimal number of words and drawings, diagrams, or symbols to respond to questions that require writing. Example: Question 1—A student might respond to this question by writing *factored form* $(x + 4)(x + 2) = $ *expanded form* $(x^2 + 6x + 8)$ under the heading *Distributive*, and $5x(2x - 4) = (2x - 4)5x$ under the heading *Commutative*.

TEACHING THE INVESTIGATION

3.1 • Walking Together

This problem expands students' understanding of equivalent expressions. Students apply the distributive and commutative properties to find an efficient expression for calculating the total amount of money raised in a walkathon. The objective is for students to articulate their reasoning, orally and in writing, as they become familiar with the symbolic techniques that can be used to show that expressions are equivalent. Using the proper names for the properties is secondary to this objective. Note that in this problem, expressions involve only positive quantities.

Launch

Use students' experiences in the previous investigation to review the terms *factored form* and *expanded form,* connecting each form with finding the area of a rectangle. Use the example in the student edition, which demonstrates the equivalence of $4(5 + x)$ and $20 + 4x$, to introduce the formal name of the distributive property. Emphasize that the distributive property says two things:

■ You can go from $4(5 + x)$ to $20 + 4x$ by multiplying.

■ You can go from $20 + 4x$ to $4(5 + x)$ by factoring.

The distributive property describes a special relationship between sums and products. Briefly discuss how the words *term, factor, product,* and *sum* are used in the distributive property. This language can be helpful to students for explaining their reasoning, although it is not necessary.

Take time to have students write and check their own numerical examples to demonstrate the validity of the distributive property; their examples might involve fractions, integers, or whole numbers. Then ask them to think of realistic situations that can be represented by their numerical examples.

> In your example, is one form of the expression more useful or convenient to use than the other?

Introduce the commutative properties, and tell the story of the walkathon. (Some students may remember studying a similar problem in the grade 7 unit *Moving Straight Ahead.* In that unit, they found expressions for the money raised by individual participants. In this problem, they find the total raised by a three-person team.)

> Have you ever participated in a walkathon or some other event that raised money through pledges? How did it work? What was the goal?

> Can you tell by looking at the information about Leanne's, Gilberto's, and Alana's pledges who will raise the most money? Can you determine the total amount of money that will be raised by the team?

Make sure the class understands that since the three students will be walking as a team, they will all walk the same distance. When students have had a chance to familiarize themselves with the situation and to verbalize that they need to know the distance walked by each student and the number of sponsors each student has, explain that they will be searching for ways to write expressions that contain this information.

> As you work, keep in mind that there are often equivalent ways to write an expression and that one might be more convenient to use than another.

Have students explore the problem in pairs.

For the Teacher: *Commutative* versus *Rearrangement*

The word *commutative* is not generally in students' everyday vocabulary. The commutative property is a very intuitive concept for students, but calling it by a strange-sounding name can make students feel as though they are missing some understanding of the property.

Some teachers prefer to use the term *rearrangement* because it helps convey the essential meaning of the properties: $a + b = b + a$ and $ab = ba$. Once their students feel comfortable with the concept, these teachers begin to use the more common term *commutative* to refer to it.

Explore

Ask students to help each other make sense of the expressions they produce.

If students have difficulty with question 1 of part B, help to guide their thinking.

> How much will Leanne raise per mile from each of her sponsors? *($1)*
> How many sponsors does Leanne have? *(16)*
>
> So, how much will she raise for walking 1 mile? *($16)*

In part C, students may find it challenging to show that their two expressions are equivalent. Try to let them arrive at a solution through their discussion with other students to help them develop a better understanding of equivalent expressions. If they still need assistance, use the context to help them add such like terms as $16x$, $7(2x)$, and $11(0.5x)$.

> How much money will Leanne raise if she walks 5 miles? How much will she and Gilberto raise together if they walk 5 miles?
>
> Is there more than one way to compute this? Could you use the distributive property? Do the terms $16x$ and $14x$ have a common factor? Can you factor it out?

The follow-up offers more practice with these ideas. Have students work on the follow-up questions as they finish the problem, or assign them as homework.

Summarize

Have students share their equations for the total amount the walkathon team will raise.

> **What ways do you know for checking whether two expressions are equivalent?**

Students will probably suggest making graphs or tables or substituting a few values into each expression. They may articulate some of their own rules, as well as their present understanding of the distributive property. Encourage such explanations as the following:

- When there are several things in parentheses to be added and a factor outside the parentheses, each thing must be multiplied by the factor outside the parentheses.

- When there are a certain number of x's and another number of x's, they can be combined by adding the numbers.

- When you add or multiply two quantities, it does not matter which one you start with.

You might insert vocabulary words such as *term* in place of *thing* without disrupting the flow of ideas.

> **Use one of your expressions for the amount the team will raise to find the team's earnings if the students walk 5 miles and if they walk 8 miles.**
>
> **Which expression did you use, and why?**

Discuss the advantages and disadvantages of each expression. More simplified expressions are usually easier to use for calculating specific values of the variable, but they often don't contain as much information about the context as do more complex expressions.

Go over the follow-up questions. Then, to assess students' understanding, write a few expressions on the board, several of which are equivalent. Ask students to identify the expressions that are not equivalent to any other expression in the list. For example:

$2x + 3 + 7x$	$9x + 3$	$2x + 10x$
$2(x + 3) + 7x$	$3(3x + 1)$	$7x + 2x + 3$	$2x(3 + 7x)$

Listen to how students talk about the expressions. Do they recognize the like terms? Do they understand the implication of the parentheses? Do they relate to the expressions in terms of some invented context? Do they suggest various ways to manipulate the expressions? Perhaps they will recognize that some of the expressions are linear and some are quadratic, and realize that this means they cannot be equivalent.

Presenting a short list of expressions such as that shown above makes an effective class opener, giving students an opportunity to talk about the meaning of the symbols and to connect new knowledge to the interpretation of the expressions. Such experiences will help students move into a world of symbols independent of context.

For the Teacher: Testing Equivalence Using a Calculator

In part C, students are asked to compare the expressions by making tables or graphs. The graphing calculator can be used to test the equivalence of two expressions. The procedure below shows how to produce two tables on a TI-80 graphing calculator. You might have students do this in class as you ask questions about what they are observing.

■ Enter the equations $y = 16x + 7(2x) + 11(5 + 0.5x)$ and $y = 35.5x + 55$ as Y1 and Y2, respectively.

■ Press [2nd] [WINDOW] to access the TABLE SETUP menu. Set TBLMIN to 0 and ΔTBL to 1.

■ Press [2nd] [GRAPH] to display the tables. Use the arrow keys to scroll down the lists of values and to move between the Y1 and Y2 columns.

What do you observe about the Y1 and Y2 columns? *(They contain the same values.)*

Use the arrow keys to scroll down. Do the Y1 and Y2 columns continue to be the same? *(yes)* What does that mean? *(The expressions are probably equivalent.)*

X	Y1
0	55
1	90.5
2	126
3	161.5
4	197
5	232.5
X=0	

X	Y2
0	55
1	90.5
2	126
3	161.5
4	197
5	232.5
Y2=55	

Students can also graph the equations.

■ Press [WINDOW] to access the WINDOW menu. Adjust the window settings by entering appropriate values such as XMIN=0, XMAX=10, XSCL=1, YMIN=0, YMAX=500, and YSCL=50.

■ Press [GRAPH].

What do you observe? *(A single line.)* Why do you see only one line when there are two equations being graphed? *(The two equations are equivalent.)*

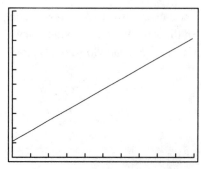

3.2 • Estimating Profit

In this problem, students consider the complications that arise when expressions involve subtraction. They explore two ideas: that subtracting several quantities is equivalent to adding all the quantities to be subtracted and then subtracting the total, and that reversing the order of subtraction does not create an equivalent expression. (These ideas were first discussed in the grade 7 unit *Accentuate the Negative*.)

Launch

Talk with the class about real-world situations that involve expenses and income.

> Have you ever kept the budget for a club, balanced a checkbook, helped plan the expenses for a trip, or tried to figure out exactly how you spent your allowance or the money you earned from a part-time job?

Point out that each of these situations begins with a set amount of money from which expenses are subtracted. Pose a simple problem to introduce the idea of a negative sign in front of a set of parentheses.

> Suppose we start with a balance of $155.75 in a checking account and write two checks, one for $14.50 and one for $45.00. Write an expression we could use to calculate the new balance. Is there more than one way to do this?

There are two obvious methods for calculating the balance.

- $155.75 - 14.50 - 45.00 = 141.25 - 45.00 = \$96.25$
- $155.75 - (14.50 + 45.00) = 155.75 - 59.50 = \$96.25$

Ask the class to write a few other expressions, such as $15 - (6 + 9)$ and $50 - 19 - 23$, in an equivalent way. Then ask them to generalize the pattern in words. This exercise should help them to think about and understand the behavior of a negative sign in front of parentheses.

With the class, read through the estimates of expenses and income made by the organizers of the walkathon. The estimates are reproduced on Transparency 3.2A.

> Do these estimates seem reasonable? Are there any other sources of expenses or income that may have been omitted?

Listen carefully to students' answers to be sure they understand the difference between income, a "positive" amount, and expenses, a "negative" amount. Understanding this concept will help them make sense of the problem and the expressions that are presented in the follow-up.

> Which expenses and income in this problem are *constant*? In other words, which expenses and income don't depend on how many people participate? *($500 expense for advertising, $1000 income from business sponsors, and $250 expense in case of emergency)*

> Which expenses and income vary depending on the number of participants? *(expense per T-shirt and income from registration fees)*
>
> What would cause an increase in *income*? *(The more participants there are, the greater the income from registration fees.)*
>
> What would cause an increase in *expenses*? *(The more participants there are, the greater the expense for T-shirts.)*

Once students understand that income and expenses both depend on the number of children and adults who participate, they are ready to write expressions for them.

Have students work on the problem individually or in pairs. Save the follow-up until after the summary of the problem.

Explore

Students may find it helpful to organize the information that they are given into "fixed income" ($1000 from business sponsors), "income that depends on who participates" (registration fees), "fixed expenses" (advertising, preparation for emergency), and "expenses that depend on who participates" (T-shirts).

Tell students that as they work on the problem, it is important that they think about different ways to reason about the situation. Also suggest that as they write more than one expression for a certain relationship, they should ask themselves whether one version of the expression is easier to work with or to understand than another.

Students may need some prompting on distributing the negative signs.

> You have found that the income is $1000 + 5c + 15a$. How do you find the profit? *(subtract the expenses)*
>
> What are the expenses? *(750 + 6c + 8.5a)*
>
> So, how can you write an expression for calculating the profit?

Help students to understand that $1000 + 5c + 15a - 750 - 6c - 8.5a$, which represents adding each source of income and subtracting each expense, is equivalent to $(1000 + 5c + 15a) - (750 + 6c + 8.5a)$, which represents subtracting the *total* expenses from the *total* income.

Summarize

Have students share the various expressions for profit that they have written as you record them on the board.

> Can all of these expressions be equivalent? How can we check?

Distribute the work by having each student check another student's expression, substituting agreed-upon values for the numbers of adults and children.

> Does each expression give the same profit? *(They should.)*

Is this enough evidence to conclude that these expressions are equivalent? *(No; we have seen before that getting the same results for one substituted value may not indicate equivalence.)*

Can we enter these expressions into a graphing calculator and check whether all entries in the tables are equal? *(No; there are too many variables to do this.)*

Can we use the properties we know to check for equivalence?

Choose several of the expressions, and ask the class how the distributive and commutative properties can be applied to transform one expression into the other.

To lead into the follow-up, have the class evaluate the following expressions:

$$16.5 - (10 + 3) \qquad 16.5 - (10 - 3) \qquad 16.5 - 2(10 + 3)$$

Then ask them to write an expression, using parentheses, that is equivalent to each of the following:

$$^-4x - 8y \qquad ^-4x + 8y \qquad 11 - 4x - 8y \qquad 11 - 4x + 8y$$

In their previous mathematics work, students learned that $^-a = (^-1)a$. Using this idea, students can rewrite an expression of the form $^-(a + b)$ as $(^-1)(a + b)$ and then apply the distributive property. For example, $16.5 - (10 + 3) = 16.5 + (^-1)(10 + 3) = 16.5 - 10 - 3 = 3.5$.

Students should be able to generalize—verbally and perhaps symbolically—the rule for handling a negative sign in front of parentheses, $^-(a + b) = ^-1(a) + ^-1(b) = ^-a + ^-b = ^-a - b$. They do not need to be able to write this general case, but they should be able to explain the behavior of such a negative sign.

ACE questions 46 and 47, which show common mistakes made by students when finding simpler versions of the profit expression, might make a good class activity. Have students work in pairs to find the errors and make the correct statements. You might want to have a transparency ready with questions 46 and 47 so students can point out the mistakes they found and use their own words to make sense of the symbols.

Give the class time to work on the follow-up questions; you may want to assign question 5 as homework. Let students explain their answers. Questions 1–3 help students make the connection from symbols back to context.

As a final summary to emphasize the meaning of *equivalent* and the advantages of knowing a few simple ways to rewrite expressions, ask students to study some expressions you write on the board. For example, put the following expressions on the board, and ask which is the easiest and which is the most difficult to evaluate for $x = 98$.

$$2(x + 2) \qquad 4(x + 1) - 2x \qquad 2x + 4 \qquad 3(x + 30) + 2(x + 6) - 4x$$

Students will likely identify the first or the third as the easiest (for $x = 98$, the first is particularly easy to evaluate) and the last as the most difficult. All four give a result of 200.

Are all these expressions equivalent? How do you know?

Students will have various ways of addressing this. Finding the same result for one substituted value is not enough to ensure equivalency. If they substitute *other* values for x, they will find that the expressions are not all equal. If they apply the rules they know to the last expression, it can be simplified to $x + 102$.

Write the following statements on the board:

$$2 - (5 + 7) \text{ and } 2 - 5 + 7 \qquad 4 - 2x - 10 \text{ and } 4 - 2(x - 5)$$

> Are these pairs of expressions equivalent? Why or why not?

Neither pair of expressions is equivalent; have students explain why.

> Write an expression that *is* equivalent to the first expression in each pair. *[2 – 5 – 7 and 4 – 2(x + 5)]*

You might ask students to make up their own pairs of expressions that are or are not equivalent.

To help students see the connection between distributing a number and distributing a negative sign over a sum of terms, ask them whether there is any way in which the following two rules are similar:

$$a(b + c + d) = ab + ac + ad \qquad \text{and} \qquad t - (p + q + r + s) = t - p - q - r - s$$

They are, in fact, both examples of the distributive property. In the first rule, all terms in the parentheses are multiplied by a. In the second rule, all terms in the parentheses are multiplied by $^-1$. It's important that students see that every new rule is not necessarily a new idea, but may be an extension or a particular case of something they already know.

To keep the idea of equivalence fresh, pose the following task.

> Calculate the value of the following expressions for $x = 1$.
>
> $$\frac{3 + 6x}{2} \qquad 1.5 + 3x \qquad \frac{9x}{2} \qquad 3 + 3x \qquad 3(0.5 + x)$$
>
> Which of these expressions are equivalent? *(The first, second, and fifth expressions are equivalent.)* How do you know?

3.3 • Finding the Area of a Trapezoid

In this problem, students connect their experience with number properties to finding formulas for area. They are encouraged to observe how applying their new knowledge gives them insight and power in working with complex formulas. Rearranging symbols not only creates new expressions, but can offer new ways of looking at a problem.

Launch

The problem illustrates three methods for finding the area of a trapezoid. Students are to determine the reasoning underlying each method and then show that the expressions for finding the area are equivalent.

You might briefly check what students recall about finding the areas of plane figures. (Students found the area of triangles, rectangles, and parallelograms in the grade 6 unit *Covering and Surrounding*.)

> How can you find the area of a rectangle? A triangle? A parallelogram?

Have students draw sketches to illustrate their methods, and review the formulas that they know. They should recall that the area of a rectangle is base times height and that the area of a triangle is half the base times the height, or $\frac{1}{2}bh$. The class may need prompting to recall how to find the area of a parallelogram; the formula is the same as that for a rectangle.

> How can you find the area of a trapezoid using the formulas you know for other figures? Remember that a *trapezoid* is a quadrilateral with one pair of parallel sides.

Give students time to share their ideas; they may or may not present a correct formula.

Have students begin work on the problem individually and then share their ideas and explore the follow-up in groups of two or three.

Explore

Ask students to illustrate anything they do to analyze Tua's, Sam's, and Carlos's methods.

Encourage those who finish the problem and the follow-up early to look for their own ways to express the area of the trapezoid. Labsheet 3.3 contains copies of the trapezoid; students may want to cut these out and experiment with them, subdividing trapezoids and rearranging the parts. You might distribute large sheets of paper to those who have interesting explanations; their work can be shared during the summary. Ask students to label their drawings with symbols so that they can connect their formulas to the parts of the diagrams.

Summarize

Have students explain how they arrived at a symbolic expression for each method. Ask whether others found different expressions or the same expression and whether they thought about the problem in a different way.

Some explanations for how the three students reasoned are as follows:

- Tua divided the trapezoid into two triangles, one with base a and one with base b and each with a height of h. The area of the trapezoid is equal to the sum of the areas of the triangles.

- Sam added an identical trapezoid to make a parallelogram with base $a + b$ and height h. The area of the parallelogram is $(a + b)h$, which is *double* the area of the trapezoid.

- Carlos cut the trapezoid horizontally and rearranged the pieces to make a parallelogram with base $b + a$ and height $\frac{1}{2}h$.

Have groups share their ideas about follow-up question 1. If their explanations do not focus on the form of the symbolic expressions, draw their attention to the form of Natasha's answer.

In the expression $\frac{1}{2}h(b-a) + ha$ (Natasha's method), the term $\frac{1}{2}h(b-a)$ implies a triangle with base $b-a$ and height h. Where is this triangle on the diagram of the trapezoid?

The term ha implies a rectangular area with base a and height h. Where is this rectangle on the diagram of the trapezoid?

The diagram below shows the related triangle and rectangle.

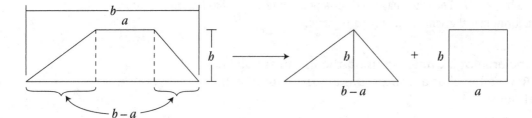

Ask how students know that Natasha's expression is equivalent to all the expressions they found in Problem 3.3. Then ask:

If we substituted values for a, b, and h in all of the formulas, should we find the same area? *(Yes, because we know all the expressions are equivalent.)*

If some students have devised their own methods, have them share them with the class. You may want to make transparent copies of the trapezoids from Labsheet 3.3 for demonstrating the various methods.

To assess students' understanding, you might offer another expression for the area and ask the class how they could reason about the area to produce it.

Another way to look at this area produces the expression $bh - \frac{1}{2}(b-a)h$.

What does the form of this answer imply about the way the person looked at the problem? *(This looks like a rectangular area, bh, minus a triangular area.)*

How could we use the diagram of the trapezoid to include a rectangle with area bh? What action is modeled by subtracting the second expression?

The following diagram represents the expression $bh - \frac{1}{2}(b-a)h$.

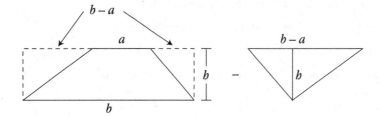

3.4 • Writing Quadratic Expressions

In the unit *Frogs, Fleas, and Painted Cubes*, students discovered and formalized the characteristics of quadratic relationships, and they worked with quadratic expressions in both factored form and expanded form. However, the investigations into the equivalence of these forms were strictly informal. In this problem, students will use tables, graphs, and the distributive property to check the equivalence of quadratic expressions.

Launch

You might begin by writing two equivalent quadratic expressions on the board, such as $x(10 - x)$ and $10x - x^2$.

> Are these expressions equivalent? Why or why not? *(Students should recognize that the distributive property can be applied to show that the expressions are equivalent.)*
>
> Describe the graph of the related equations, $y = x(10 - x)$ and $y = 10x - x^2$.
>
> Which equation did you use to figure out what the graph would look like? Why?

Students' responses will reveal what they recall from their previous work. They may remember, for example, that a negative coefficient of the x^2 term indicates that the graph will be a parabola that opens downward.

Talk about the table showing the results of the games played by a five-team soccer league. Be sure everyone understands how to read the table and why some entries are dashes.

> How can you tell from the table how many games were played in all? *(We know that the total number of games is 20 because that's how many cells contain an L or a W. Or, it is $5 \times 5 - 5$: there are 5×5 entries, minus the 5 entries that represent a team playing itself.)*
>
> What we want to find is a way to determine the number of games played in all by a league with *any* number of teams.

Explain that as students investigate, they have two goals: to find a rule or pattern that will help them to write an expression for the number of games played by a league with n teams, and to decide whether different expressions representing this are equivalent.

Have students work in groups of two to four on the problem and the follow-up.

Explore

Parts A, B, and C direct students to write expressions based on thinking about the problem in three ways:

- as a pattern in a table, $n^2 - n$ or $n(n - 1)$

Number of teams	Number of games	Pattern
2	2	2×1
3	6	3×2
4	12	4×3
5	20	5×4
6	30	6×5

- as the logical result of a calculation (n choices for the home team and $n - 1$ choices for the visiting team), $n(n - 1)$

- as a visual pattern in a grid; the number of rows times the number of columns minus the cells on the diagonal, $n(n) - n$

Groups will end up with two or three equivalent expressions, depending on whether they simplify $n(n) - n$ to $n^2 - n$ or treat them as separate expressions.

In part A, group members could share the work, with different students counting the number of games played by each size league. For each number of teams, students should make a table similar to the one for a five-team league, with dashes on the diagonal.

As you see various groups being successful with each method, you might give them blank transparencies or large sheets of paper for recording their ideas.

For the follow-up, have students read individually the discussion preceding the questions, or talk as a class about the material and offer more examples. Help students recognize that multiplying factors containing two terms (binomials) is a triple application of the distributive property.

Summarize

Have groups share their expressions from parts A, B, and C and explain the reasoning or the patterns that led to their expressions. Try to obtain all three common forms of the expression, $n(n - 1)$, $n^2 - n$, and $n(n) - n$. Point out again that while the tables and graphs related to equivalent expressions are identical, the equivalent expressions represent different conceptualizations of the problem.

To make a connection to students' earlier work, pose one of the handshake problems from *Frogs, Fleas, and Painted Cubes*.

> If the *n* players on one team shake hands with every member on another team of *n* players, how many handshakes are exchanged? *[There are $n(n - 1)$, or $n^2 - n$, handshakes in all.]*

Students should recognize that although the expressions for the number of games played by an *n*-team league and the number of handshakes exchanged between two *n*-player teams represent information from two different contexts, they are identical.

Review the follow-up questions, asking for an equivalent expression for each of those given. If students have difficulty seeing the equivalence, you can return to an area model for the distributive property. Sketch a rectangle on the board; the following relates to question 2.

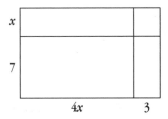

How can we express the area of the large rectangle?

Students should suggest two methods: multiplying length by width, resulting in the expression $(4x + 3)(x + 7)$, and adding the areas of the smaller rectangles, resulting in the expression $4x^2 + 3x + 28x + 21$, or $4x^2 + 31x + 21$.

As a review, ask the class to use any method they want to show that the following pairs of expressions are equivalent:

- $x(x + 5)$ and $x^2 + 5x$
- $3x(8 + x)$ and $24x + 3x^2$
- $(x + 2)(x + 5)$ and $x^2 + 7x + 10$

Additional Answers

Answers to Problem 3.1

C. 1. Possible answer: $16x + 7(2x) + 11(5 + 0.5x) = 16x + 14x + 55 + 5.5x = 35.5x + 55$

2. The table contains the same values for the expressions, and the graphs are the same.

x	$16x + 7(2x) + 11(5 + 0.5x)$	$35.5x + 55$
0	$16(0) + 7(0) + 11(5 + 0) = 55$	$35.5(0) + 55 = 55$
1	$16(1) + 7(2) + 11(5 + 0.5) = 90.5$	$35.5(1) + 55 = 90.5$
2	$16(2) + 7(4) + 11(5 + 1) = 126$	$35.5(2) + 55 = 126$
3	$16(3) + 7(6) + 11(5 + 1.5) = 161.5$	$35.5(3) + 55 = 161.5$
4	$16(4) + 7(8) + 11(5 + 2) = 197$	$35.5(4) + 55 = 197$

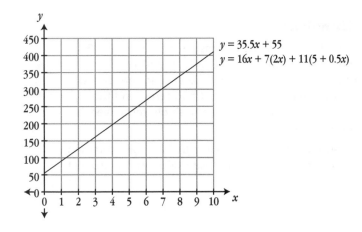

Answers to Problem 3.1 Follow-Up

8. not equivalent; When $x = 0$, $3x + 8$ equals 8 and $8x + 3$ equals 3.

9. equivalent; $5x + 3x + 4x = (5 + 3 + 4)x = 12x$ and $4x + 5x + 3x = (4 + 5 + 3)x = 12x$

10. equivalent; $6 + 2t = 2t + 6 = 2(t + 3)$

11. equivalent; $2(L + 2) + 2W = 2L + 4 + 2W = 2L + 2W + 4$

12. equivalent; $2L + 2W + 4 = 2(L + W + 2)$

Answers to Problem 3.2

F. $[1000 + 5(75) + 15(100)] - [750 + 6(75) + 8.50(100)] = (1000 + 375 + 1500) - (750 + 450 + 850) = 2875 - 2050 = \$825$, and $250 - 75 + 6.50(100) = 250 - 75 + 650 = \$825$; This shows that the expressions may be equivalent, but it doesn't prove they are.

G. The short form is easier to evaluate, but the numbers 250, $^-1$, and 6.50 do not directly reveal information about the specific sources of income and expenses.

Answers to Problem 3.2 Follow-Up

4. They are not equivalent; explanations will vary. Students might substitute the same value into the expressions, show that the related tables or graphs ($y = 3 - 2x$ decreases from left to right, $y = 2x - 3$ increases from left to right) are different, or apply the commutative property: $3 - 2x = 3 + {}^-2x = {}^-2x + 3 \neq 2x - 3$.

5.   a. $(9x + 15) - (8 + 2x) = 9x + 15 - 8 - 2x = 7x + 7$, or $7(x + 1)$

   b. $(7x - 12) - (9x + 15) = 7x - 12 - 9x - 15 = {}^-2x - 27$

   c. $(14r + 9t + 15) + (23 - 9r + 3t) = 14r + 9t + 15 + 23 - 9r + 3t = 5r + 12t + 38$

   d. $19 - 12x + 20 + 9x = 39 - 3x$

Answers to Problem 3.3 Follow-Up

1.   a. Natasha's drawing may have looked like the one below, in which the trapezoid is divided into three sections with vertical lines. The area of the trapezoid is equal to the area of a triangle with base $b - a$, plus a rectangle with base a and height h. The area of the trapezoid is thus $\frac{1}{2}(b - a)h + ah$, or $\frac{1}{2}h(b - a) + ha$.

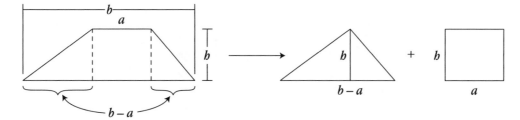

Answers to Problem 3.4 Follow-Up

7.   a. If each factor contains the sum or difference of two terms (as in questions 2, 3, and 4), use the distributive property to multiply one factor by the other. Use one expression as a factor and distribute it over the sum or difference in the second expression. If one factor contains the sum or difference of two terms and the other factor is a single term (as in question 1), distribute the single term over the sum or difference in the other expression.

   b. To factor an expression with two terms (as in questions 5 and 6), look for a common factor in each term. Remove that factor, and rewrite the expression as the product of factors.

ACE Answers

Applications

10a. $5000 - 50(75 - 25) = 5000 - 50(50) = 5000 - 2500 = 2500$; Work within the parentheses first, multiply the result by 50, and subtract this number from 5000.

10b. $5000 - 3750 + 50T$, or $1250 + 50T$; For $T = 25$, $1250 + 50(25) = 1250 + 1250 = 2500$. The order in which the operations are performed has changed because there are no parentheses: multiply T by 50 and add the result to 1250. The operations are different, but you still multiply before adding.

10c. The simpler form is easier to evaluate.

Connections

26a.

x	10 − 5x	5x − 10
-3	25	-25
-2	20	-20
-1	15	-15
0	10	-10
1	5	-5
2	0	0
3	-5	5

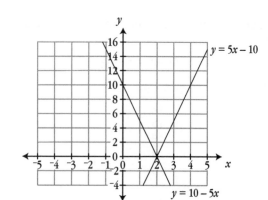

26b. The expressions are not equivalent because the table values are different and the graphs are separate lines; one has a negative slope and one has a positive slope.

26c. $10 - 5x = {}^-5x + 10 \neq 5x - 10$

27a.

x	(3x + 4) + (2x − 3)	5x + 1
-3	-14	-14
-2	-9	-9
-1	-4	-4
0	1	1
1	6	6
2	11	11
3	16	16

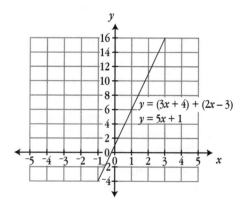

27b. The expressions are probably equivalent because the table values are the same and the graph is a single line.

27c. $(3x + 4) + (2x - 3) = 3x + 2x + 4 - 3 = (3 + 2)x + 1 = 5x + 1$

28a.

x	$9x - 5(x - 3) - 20$	$5 - 4x$
$^-3$	$^-17$	17
$^-2$	$^-13$	13
$^-1$	$^-9$	9
0	$^-5$	5
1	$^-1$	1
2	3	$^-3$
3	7	$^-7$

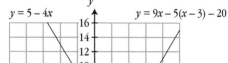
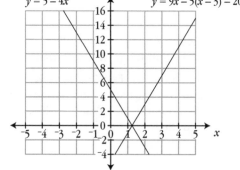

28b. The expressions are not equivalent because the table values are different and the graphs are separate lines.

28c. $9x - 5(x - 3) - 20 = 9x - 5x + 15 - 20 = 4x - 5 \neq 5 - 4x$

29a.

x	$(10x - 5) - (4x + 2)$	$10x - 5 - 4x + 2$
$^-3$	$^-25$	$^-21$
$^-2$	$^-19$	$^-15$
$^-1$	$^-13$	$^-9$
0	$^-7$	$^-3$
1	$^-1$	3
2	5	9
3	11	15

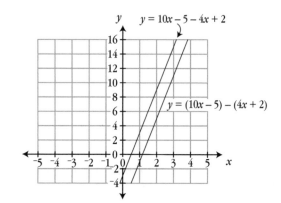

29b. The expressions are not equivalent because the table values are different and the graphs are separate lines.

29c. $(10x - 5) - (4x + 2) = 10x - 5 - 4x - 2 \neq 10x - 5 - 4x + 2$ (or $6x - 7 \neq 6x - 3$)

33a. Either form can be used, but it is easier to tell whether there will be a maximum or minimum point from the expanded form. If the coefficient of x^2 is positive, the graph has a minimum point. If the coefficient of x^2 is negative, the graph has a maximum point.

33b. The y-intercept can be read directly from the expanded form by substituting 0 for x; it is the constant term in the expanded form. The x-intercepts can be easily determined from the factored form because they are the values that make the factors equal to 0.

33c. The line of symmetry is the vertical line perpendicular to the x-axis through the point halfway between the x-intercepts. This point can be found more easily from the factored form.

33d. The x-coordinate of the maximum or minimum point lies on the line of symmetry, which crosses the x-axis halfway between the x-intercepts. The factored form can be used to find the x-coordinate. To find the y-coordinate, substitute this value of x into either form.

34a. $x(x + 5)$: The x-intercepts are 0 and $^-5$; the y-intercept is 0.

$(2 + x)(2 + 3x)$: The x-intercepts are $^-2$ and $^-\frac{2}{3}$; the y-intercept is 4.

$(x + 2)(2x + 3)$: The x-intercepts are $^-2$ and $^-\frac{3}{2}$; the y-intercept is 6.

34b. $x(x + 5)$: The line of symmetry is the vertical line through the point halfway between 0 and -5, or $x = -\frac{5}{2}$.

$(2 + x)(2 + 3x)$: The line of symmetry is the vertical line through the point halfway between -2 and $-\frac{2}{3}$, or $x = -\frac{4}{3}$.

$(x + 2)(2x + 3)$: The line of symmetry is the vertical line through the point halfway between -2 and $-\frac{3}{2}$, or $x = -\frac{7}{4}$.

34c. $x(x + 5)$: The x-coordinate of the maximum or minimum point is $-\frac{5}{2}$, and the y-coordinate is $-\frac{5}{2}(-\frac{5}{2} + 5) = -\frac{5}{2}(\frac{5}{2}) = -\frac{25}{4}$.

$(2 + x)(2 + 3x)$: The x-coordinate of the maximum or minimum point is $-\frac{4}{3}$, and the y-coordinate is $(2 - \frac{4}{3})(2 - 4) = \frac{2}{3}(-2) = -\frac{4}{3}$.

$(x + 2)(2x + 3)$: The x-coordinate of the maximum or minimum point is $-\frac{7}{4}$, and the y-coordinate is $(-\frac{7}{4} + 2)(-\frac{7}{2} + 3) = \frac{1}{4}(-\frac{1}{2}) = -\frac{1}{8}$.

34d. $y = x(x + 5)$ $y = (2 + x)(2 + 3x)$ $y = (x + 2)(2x + 3)$

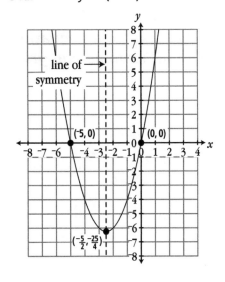

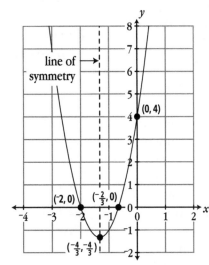

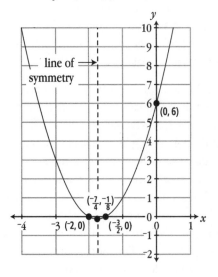

Solving Equations

In their previous mathematics work, students learned to solve simple linear equations in tabular, graphical, and symbolic ways. Rudimentary understanding of properties of equations was reinforced in *Thinking with Mathematical Models,* in which students found the equation of a line from two points on the line. In *Frogs, Fleas, and Painted Cubes,* students solved quadratic equations using tables and graphs. In this investigation, students bring together their experiences to establish systematic methods of solving equations. The ultimate goal is for students to become aware of the strengths and weaknesses of each solution method.

In Problem 4.1, Comparing Costs, students review how to solve a linear equation using both a graph and a table. Problem 4.2, Solving Linear Equations, reviews the symbolic method for solving linear equations. It asks students to supply reasons for the steps of a symbolic solution to an equation and then to connect this solution to graphical and tabular representations. In Problem 4.3, Reasoning with Symbols, students learn more about symbolic strategies for solving equations of the form $ax + b = cx + d$. Problem 4.4, Solving Quadratic Equations, offers students an introduction to symbolic solutions for equations of the form $y = ax^2 + bx$.

Mathematical and Problem-Solving Goals

- *To apply the properties for manipulating expressions to solving linear equations*

- *To solve simple quadratic equations symbolically*

- *To connect the solutions of an equation to information about its table and graph*

Materials

Problem	For students	For the teacher
All	Graphing calculators, grid paper (optional), blank transparencies and transparent grids (optional)	Transparencies: 4.1 to 4.4C, transparent grid, overhead graphing calculator (all optional)
4.2	Large sheets of paper (optional)	Pan balance (optional)

INVESTIGATION 4

Solving Equations

Solving mathematical problems often requires finding solutions to equations or inequalities. In this investigation, you will learn algebraic methods for solving linear and quadratic equations.

 4.1 Comparing Costs

Imagine that you are a creative-writing club. The club wants to publish a book of students' short stories, poems, and essays. You contact two local printers to obtain bids on the cost of printing the books.

bid 1: cost = $100 + $4 × the number of books printed
bid 2: cost = $25 + $7 × the number of books printed

In earlier units, you learned strategies for comparing the two bids. If you let x represent the number of books printed and y represent the cost in dollars, the equations become $y = 100 + 4x$ and $y = 25 + 7x$. You can use your graphing calculator to make and compare tables and graphs of these equations.

Problem 4.1

Use your graphing calculator to help answer parts A–C.

A. Make a table of x and y values for each bid. Use your table to find the number of books for which the two bids are equal. Explain your work.

B. Make a graph of the two equations. Use your graph to find the number of books for which the two bids are equal. Copy the graph onto your paper, and use it to help explain how you found your answer.

C. For what numbers of books is bid 1 less than bid 2? Explain how you found your answer.

At a Glance

Grouping:
small groups

Launch
■ Talk about the two bids and how the related linear equations might be solved.

Explore
■ Have groups of three or four explore the problem and follow-up.

Summarize
■ Ask questions to help students relate the tabular, graphic, and symbolic representations of the two bids.

■ Review the follow-up questions.

■ Talk about the various solution methods.

Answers to Problem 4.1

A. The two bids are equal when the y values for a common x value are equal. This occurs when $x = 25$ and $y = 200$, meaning the bids are both $200 for 25 books.

x	$y = 100 + 4x$	$y = 25 + 7x$
10	$140	$95
15	160	130
20	180	165
25	**200**	**200**
30	220	235

B, C. See page 64m.

Assignment Choices

ACE questions 5, 16, and unassigned choices from earlier problems

4.2

Solving Linear Equations

Launch

- As a class, solve follow-up question 2 from Problem 4.1 symbolically.

- Introduce the idea of setting the bid equations equal to find the common solution.

- Have students explore the problem individually and then work in pairs.

Explore

- Have students who finish early prepare displays of the table and graph of the equation in the follow-up.

Summarize

- Discuss alternative first steps.

- Ask the class to compare the three methods: graphical, tabular, and symbolic.

Assignment Choices

ACE questions 1, 2, 11, and unassigned choices from earlier problems

---

■ **Problem 4.1 Follow-Up**

1. For each bid, find the cost of printing 75 books. Explain how you found your answers.

2. For each bid, find the greatest number of books that can be printed if the cost is not to exceed $300. Explain your answers.

3. The club decides to request bids from two more printers.

bid 3: cost = $8 × the number of books printed
bid 4: cost = $30 + $6 × the number of books printed

For what number of books are these two bids equal? Explain how you found your answer.

 Solving Linear Equations

You know how to solve equations by using your calculator to make and compare graphs and tables. However, you can solve many equations without using a calculator by operating on the symbols. In Problem 4.1, the equation for bid 1 is $y = 100 + 4x$, where y is the cost and x is the number of books printed. To find out how many books can be printed for $300, you can solve the equation $300 = 100 + 4x$ for the variable x.

In your earlier mathematics work, you learned that to solve linear equations such as $300 = 100 + 4x$, you need to *undo* the mathematical operations until x is alone on one side of the equation. To make sure the sides of the equation remain equal, you must apply any mathematical operation to *both* sides. This *symbolic method* of solution is illustrated in the example below.

$$300 = 100 + 4x$$
$$300 - 100 = 100 - 100 + 4x$$ Since 100 is added to $4x$, subtract 100 from
$$200 = 4x$$ *both sides* of the equation.

$$\frac{200}{4} = \frac{4x}{4}$$ Since x is multiplied by 4, divide *both sides* by 4.

$$50 = x$$ Now x is alone on one side of the equation. It is easy to see that the solution is 50. This means that 50 books can be printed for $300.

In Problem 4.1, you found the number of books for which the two bids are equal. This is the same as solving the equation $100 + 4x = 25 + 7x$ for the variable x. Unlike the previous example, this equation has an x on both sides. However, the method for solving the equation is the same: *undo* the mathematical operations until the variable is alone on one side of the equation, making sure to apply all mathematical operations to *both sides* of the equation.

54 Say It with Symbols

Answers to Problem 4.1 Follow-Up

1. bid 1: 100 + 4(75) = $400, bid 2: 25 + 7(75) = $550 (Students might also find these values from the table or the graph.)

2. The greatest number of books that can be printed is 50 for bid 1 and 39 for bid 2. Explanations will vary. Students might extend their tables or graphs, use trial and error, or apply their growing knowledge of methods for solving linear equations.

3. The related equations are $y = 8x$ and $y = 30 + 6x$. The two bids are equal when $x = 15$ and $y = 120$, meaning they are both $120 for 15 books. Explanations will vary; students may use tables, graphs, or begin to see a pattern and solve the equation $8x = 30 + 6x$ symbolically.

Problem 4.2

The example below shows one way to solve the equation $100 + 4x = 25 + 7x$.

$$100 + 4x = 25 + 7x$$
$$100 + 4x - 4x = 25 + 7x - 4x \qquad 1.$$
$$100 = 25 + 3x$$
$$100 - 25 = 25 + 3x - 25 \qquad 2.$$
$$75 = 3x$$
$$\frac{75}{3} = \frac{3x}{3} \qquad 3.$$
$$25 = x$$

A. Supply an explanation for each numbered step in the above solution to $100 + 4x = 25 + 7x$.

B. The solution above begins by subtracting $4x$ from both sides of the equation. Show a solution that begins with a different step.

C. How can you check that $x = 25$ is the correct solution? Show that your method works.

■ Problem 4.2 Follow-Up

Solutions to linear equations are often given in fewer steps, with some of the details omitted. It is assumed that the reader can fill in the gaps. In this solution to $11x - 12 = 30 + 5x$, some of the details have been omitted.

$$11x - 12 = 30 + 5x$$
$$11x = 42 + 5x$$
$$6x = 42$$
$$x = 7$$

1. Copy the solution above, filling in the details that were omitted.

2. How can you check that $x = 7$ is the correct solution? Demonstrate your method.

3. Explain how you could use a graph and a table to solve the equation $11x - 12 = 30 + 5x$.

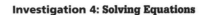

Answers to Problem 4.2

A. 1. Subtract $4x$ from both sides.

2. Subtract 25 from both sides.

3. Divide both sides by 3.

B, C. See page 64n.

Answers to Problem 4.2 Follow-Up

See page 64n.

Reasoning with Symbols

Grouping: *individuals, then small groups*

Launch

- Review logical first steps for solving linear equations.

- Have students begin work individually, then share methods and do the follow-up in groups of two or three.

Explore

- If students have trouble writing general solution strategies, have them look for similarities in their solutions to A–D.

Summarize

- Discuss the general strategies students found.

- Talk about the follow-up, having students share their equation for question 2.

4.3 **Reasoning with Symbols**

Although you can solve equations by making tables or graphs, it is often more efficient to use the symbolic method described in Problem 4.2.

> **Problem 4.3**
>
> In A–D, use the symbolic method to solve the equation.
>
> **A.** $7x + 15 = 12x + 5$ **B.** $14 - 3x = 1.5x + 5$
>
> **C.** $^-3x + 5 = 2x - 10$ **D.** $3 + 5(x + 2) = 7x - 1$
>
> **E.** Check your solutions to the equations in A–D.
>
> **F.** Look over your work for A–D. Record any general strategies that seem to work well in solving linear equations.

■ Problem 4.3 Follow-Up

1. In a–c, the given equation is related to the equation $y = 7.5x - 23.5$. Explain what question the solution to the given equation answers. For example, the solution to $7.5x - 23.5 = 10$ answers the question "What is the value of x in the equation $y = 7.5x - 23.5$ when $y = 10$?" Then use a table or a graph to solve the equation, and explain how you found your solution.

    a. $7.5x - 23.5 = 51.5$ **b.** $7.5x - 23.5 = 0$ **c.** $7.5x - 23.5 = ^-30$

2. Write a linear equation with a solution of $x = 2$. Do you think everyone in your class wrote the same equation? Explain.

3. The school choir is selling boxes of greeting cards to raise money for a trip. The equation for the profit in dollars, P, in terms of the number of boxes sold, x, is

    $$P = 3x - (100 + 2x).$$

    a. How many boxes must the choir sell to make a $200 profit? Explain how you found your answer.

    b. How many boxes must the choir sell to break even? Explain how you found your answer.

Assignment Choices

ACE questions 3, 4, 12, 13, 20, 21, and unassigned choices from earlier problems

Answers to Problem 4.3

A–E. See page 64o.

F. Possible answer: Isolate the variable on one side of the equation by adding or subtracting terms to get like terms on the same side. Then divide by the coefficient of x to get the solution.

Answers to Problem 4.3 Follow-Up

See page 64o.

Different ways of thinking about a problem can lead to different methods for solving it. For example, finding the x-intercepts of the graph of $y = x^2 + 5x$ is the same as solving the equation $x^2 + 5x = 0$.

In earlier units, you solved quadratic equations by using tables and graphs. For example, to solve $x^2 + 5x = 0$, you can trace a graph of $y = x^2 + 5x$ to find x values for which $y = 0$. Or you can make a table of values and look for the x values that correspond to a y value of 0.

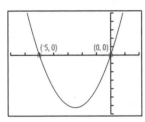

x	y
-7	14
-6	6
-5	0
-4	-4
-3	-6
-2	-6
-1	-4
0	0
1	6
2	14
3	24

The solutions to $x^2 + 5x = 0$ are called the **roots** of the equation $y = x^2 + 5x$. A quadratic equation may have zero, one, or two roots. If r is a root of an equation, then the point $(r, 0)$ is an x-intercept of the graph.

Algebra provides important tools that can help you solve quadratic equations such as $x^2 + 5x = 0$ without using tables or graphs. This problem illustrates a symbolic method for finding the roots of some quadratic equations.

Solving Quadratic Equations

At a Glance

Grouping:
pairs

Launch

- Introduce the idea of solving a quadratic equation by first factoring it.

- Have pairs explore the problem and follow-up.

Explore

- Encourage students to solve the equations by first factoring them.

- Offer students who finish early other equations to solve.

Summarize

- Discuss the strategies that students used.

- Talk about other quadratic equations and how they might be solved.

Assignment Choices

ACE questions 6–10, 14, 15, 17–19, 22–27, and unassigned choices from earlier problems

Assessment

It is appropriate to use Check-Up 2 after this problem.

Problem 4.4

A. The expression $x^2 + 3x$ is in expanded form. Write an equivalent expression in factored form.

B. Find all possible solutions to the equation $x^2 + 3x = 0$. Explain how you know you have found all the solutions.

C. What are the x-intercepts of $y = x^2 + 3x$? Explain how your answers to part B can help you answer this question.

D. Which form of the expression $x^2 + 3x$, the expanded form or the factored form, is more useful for finding the roots, or x-intercepts, of the equation $y = x^2 + 3x$? Explain your reasoning.

E. In 1 and 2, an equation is given for both the factored form and the expanded form of a quadratic expression. Find the roots, or x-intercepts, of the equation without making a table or a graph, and tell which form of the equation you used to find your answer.

    1. $y = 4x^2 - 8x$ or $y = 4x(x - 2)$ **2.** $y = 6x(5 - 2x)$ or $y = 30x - 12x^2$

F. In 1–3, solve the equation by first factoring the quadratic expression.

    1. $x^2 + 4.5x = 0$ **2.** $x^2 - 9x = 0$ **3.** $^-x^2 + 10x = 0$

■ **Problem 4.4 Follow-Up**

1. Check your answers to part F without using a table or a graph.

2. Check your answers to part F by making graphs and finding the x-intercepts.

3. **a.** For each expression below, find an equivalent expression in expanded form.
    b. Which form of the expression would you use to predict the x-intercepts of the related graph? Find the x-intercepts and explain your reasoning.
      i. $(2x + 1)(x + 5)$ **ii.** $(x + 2)(x - 2)$

4. Use the diagram below to find the linear factors of $x^2 + 8x + 12$. Use the factors to solve the equation $x^2 + 8x + 12 = 0$.

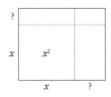

$$x^2 + 8x + 12 = (x + ?)(x + ?)$$

Answers to Problem 4.4

A. $x(x + 3)$

B. For $x^2 + 3x$ to equal 0, one or both of the factors of $x(x + 3)$ must equal 0. So, $x = 0$ or $x + 3 = 0$. Thus, $x = 0$ or $x = ^-3$.

C. The x-intercepts are the points on the graph where $y = 0$. In part B, the values of x when $y = 0$ were found to be 0 and $^-3$, so the x-intercepts are (0, 0) and $(^-3, 0)$.

D. The factored form is easier because the product of the two factors must be 0, which can happen only if one or both of the factors equal 0.

E, F. See page 64q.

Answers to Problem 4.4 Follow-Up

See page 64q.

Applications · Connections · Extensions

As you work on these ACE questions, use your calculator whenever you need it.

Applications

In 1–10, solve the equation by using the symbolic method. Check your solution by making tables or graphs with your calculator.

1. $6x + 10 = 4x + 18$

2. $3x + 47 = 7x + 7$

3. $10 - 5x = 10x + 5(x - 6)$

4. $^-13x + 36 = 20x - 30$

5. $8.3x - 10.75 = 51.5$

6. $x(x - 7) = 0$

7. $x^2 + 1.5x = 0$

8. $x^2 + 6x + 8 = 0$

9. $x^2 + 2x + 1 = 0$

10. $8x - x^2 = 0$

11. The student council is sponsoring a T-shirt sale. They plan to take orders in advance so they know how many T-shirts to have printed. They made the following estimates of expenses and income for their sale:

- Expense of $350 for advertising
- Expense of $3.25 for each T-shirt
- Income of $10 for each T-shirt
- Income of $200 from a local business in exchange for printing the business's logo on the back of the T-shirts

a. Write an equation for the profit, P, the student council will make if they sell n T-shirts.

b. How many T-shirts must the student council sell to break even? Describe at least three ways you could find the answer to this question. Use one of the ways to find the solution.

3.
$$10 - 5x = 10x + 5(x - 6)$$
$$10 - 5x = 10x + 5x - 30$$
$$10 - 5x = 15x - 30$$
$$10 + 30 - 5x = 15x - 30 + 30$$
$$40 - 5x = 15x$$
$$40 - 5x + 5x = 15x + 5x$$
$$40 = 20x$$
$$\frac{40}{20} = \frac{20x}{20}$$
$$2 = x$$

4.
$$^-13x + 36 = 20x - 30$$
$$^-13x + 13x + 36 = 20x + 13x - 30$$
$$36 = 33x - 30$$
$$36 + 30 = 33x - 30 + 30$$
$$66 = 33x$$
$$\frac{66}{33} = \frac{33x}{33}$$
$$2 = x$$

Applications

1.
$$6x + 10 = 4x + 18$$
$$6x - 4x + 10 = 4x - 4x + 18$$
$$2x + 10 = 18$$
$$2x + 10 - 10 = 18 - 10$$
$$2x = 8$$
$$\frac{2x}{2} = \frac{8}{2}$$
$$x = 4$$

2.
$$3x + 47 = 7x + 7$$
$$3x - 3x + 47 = 7x - 3x + 7$$
$$47 = 4x + 7$$
$$47 - 7 = 4x + 7 - 7$$
$$40 = 4x$$
$$\frac{40}{4} = \frac{4x}{4}$$
$$10 = x$$

3, 4. See below left.

5–10. See page 64r.

11a. Possible answers: $P = 10n + 200 - 3.25n - 350$ or $P = 6.75n - 150$

11b. To break even, income and expenses must be equal, which means profit is 0. The break-even point can be found by setting the profit equation equal to 0:
$$6.75n - 150 = 0$$
$$6.75n = 150$$
$$n \approx 22.22$$

The break-even point is about 23 T-shirts. For 23 or more T-shirts, they will make a profit. (Note: The problem could also be solved by making a table or a graph of the profit equation to see at what number of T-shirts profit becomes positive or the line crosses the x-axis.)

Connections

12a. $48 = 2s + 2(s + 2)$
$48 = 2s + 2s + 4$
$48 = 4s + 4$
$44 = 4s$
$11 = s$

12b. $48 = 4(s + 2) - 4$
$48 = 4s + 8 - 4$
$48 = 4s + 4$
$44 = 4s$
$11 = s$

12c. The answers are the same. This is because the original equations are equivalent; they express the same relationship between N and s.

13. (Note: Students might choose to solve this using a table or a graph.)
$1000 = 200 + 50(T - 70)$
$1000 = 200 + 50T - 3500$
$1000 = 50T - 3300$
$4300 = 50T$
$86 = T$
The temperature was 86°F.

14. The x-intercepts of $g = n^2 - n = n(n - 1)$ are $n = 0$ and $n = 1$. This means that for a league with 0 teams or 1 team, there are no league games.

15. The equation $0.2x(100 - x) = 0$ has solutions $x = 0$ and $x = 100$, so the x-intercepts are 0 and 100. The maximum point has an x-coordinate halfway between these two points, at $x = 50$. The y-intercept of the maximum point, or the maximum height, is $y = 0.2(50)(100 - 50) = 0.2(50)(50) = 500$ ft.

Connections

12. The equations $N = 2s + 2(s + 2)$ and $N = 4(s + 2) - 4$ represent the number of square tiles, measuring 1 foot on each side, needed to make a border for a square pool with sides of length s feet.

   a. Solve $N = 2s + 2(s + 2)$ for $N = 48$.

   b. Solve $N = 4(s + 2) - 4$ for $N = 48$.

   c. How do your answers for parts a and b compare? Why?

13. The number of visitors to a park depends on the day's high Fahrenheit temperature, T, according to the equation $V = 200 + 50(T - 70)$. If 1000 people visit the park one day, what would you predict was that day's high temperature?

14. The number of games played in a league with n teams if each team plays each of the other teams twice is $g = n^2 - n$. What are the x-intercepts of the graph of this equation? Explain what information they represent.

15. The height in feet of an arch above a point x feet from one of its bases is given by the equation $y = 0.2x(100 - x)$. What is the maximum height of the arch? Explain how you found your answer.

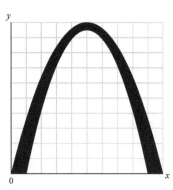

16. Below are the graphs of $y = 1.5x + 6$ and $y = -2x + 15$. The scale on the x-axis is 1, and the scale on the y-axis is 3.

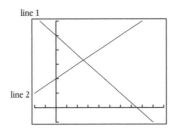

line 1

line 2

a. Match each equation, $y = 1.5x + 6$ and $y = -2x + 15$, to line 1 or line 2.

b. What are the coordinates of the point of intersection of the two lines?

c. How could you find the answer to part b without using a graph or a table?

d. What values of x satisfy the inequality $1.5x + 6 < -2x + 15$? How is your answer shown on the graph?

e. What values of x satisfy the inequality $1.5x + 6 > -2x + 15$? How is your answer shown on the graph?

17. Below is the graph of $y = x^2 - 9x$. The scale on the x-axis is 1, and the scale on the y-axis is 2. Use the graph to answer parts a–e on the next page.

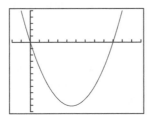

16a. The equation of line 1 is $y = -2x + 15$. The equation of line 2 is $y = 1.5x + 6$.

16b. From the graph, the coordinates are approximately $(2.6, 10)$.

16c. At the point of intersection, the equations are equal: $-2x + 15 = 1.5x + 6$, or $15 = 3.5x + 6$, or $x = \frac{9}{3.5} \approx 2.57$. For this value of x, $y \approx 1.5(2.57) + 6 \approx 9.86$.

16d. The graph of $y = 1.5x + 6$ is below the graph of $y = -2x + 15$ for values of x less than 2.57, so $1.5x + 6 < -2x + 15$ when $x < 2.57$.

16e. The graph of $y = 1.5x + 6$ is above the graph of $y = -2x + 15$ for values of x greater than 2.57, so $1.5x + 6 > -2x + 15$ when $x > 2.57$.

17a. (0, 0) and (9, 0)

17b. You could rewrite the expression in factored form and find the factors that make it equal to 0: for $x(x - 9) = 0$, $x = 0$ or $x = 9$.

17c. The values of x that satisfy $x^2 - 9x < 0$ are those associated with the portion of the graph below the x-axis, or $0 < x < 9$.

17d. The values of x that satisfy $x^2 - 9x > 0$ are those associated with the portion of the graph to the right of the line $x = 9$ or to the left of the line $x = 0$, or $x > 9$ or $x < 0$.

17e. The minimum y value, ⁻20.25, occurs when $x = 4.5$.

Extensions

18a. The solutions are $x = {}^-3$ and $x = 2$. These are the points at which the graph crosses the x-axis.

18b. The values of x that satisfy $(x + 3)(x - 2) < 0$ are ⁻3 < x < 2. This is the part of the graph below the x-axis.

18c. Possible answer: The product of two numbers is negative. This means that one factor must be negative and the other must be positive. We need to look at two cases. In the first case, $x + 3 > 0$ and $x - 2 < 0$, or $x > {}^-3$ and $x < 2$. Therefore, numbers between ⁻3 and 2 fit both conditions. In the second case, $x + 3 < 0$ and $x - 2 > 0$, or $x < {}^-3$ and $x > 2$. No number can be less than ⁻3 and greater than 2, so this case is impossible.

---

a. What are the coordinates of the x-intercepts?

b. How could you find the answer to part a without using a graph or a table?

c. What values of x satisfy the inequality $x^2 - 9x < 0$? How is your answer shown on the graph?

d. What values of x satisfy the inequality $x^2 - 9x > 0$? How is your answer shown on the graph?

e. What is the minimum y value? What x value corresponds to this minimum value?

Extensions

18. Below is the graph of $y = (x + 3)(x - 2)$. The scale on both axes is 1.

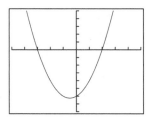

a. Solve $(x + 3)(x - 2) = 0$? How are the solutions shown on the graph?

b. What values of x satisfy the inequality $(x + 3)(x - 2) < 0$? How is your answer shown on the graph?

c. How can you find the answer to part b, without using the graph, by analyzing the inequality? (Hint: Use what you know about multiplying positive and negative numbers.)

19. Here is the graph of $y = (x + 2)(x - 1)(x - 5)$.
The scale on the x-axis is 1, and the scale on
the y-axis is 5.

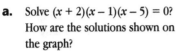

   a. Solve $(x + 2)(x - 1)(x - 5) = 0$?
How are the solutions shown on
the graph?

   b. What values of x satisfy the inequality
$(x + 2)(x - 1)(x - 5) < 0$? How is your
answer shown on the graph?

   c. How can you find the answer to part b, without using the graph, by
analyzing the inequality? (Hint: Use what you know about multiplying
positive and negative numbers.)

In 20 and 21, solve the equation and check your answer.

20. $5 + 8(x + 2) = 6(1 + x) - 1$

21. $2x - 3(x + 4) - 10 = 9 - 3(2 + 2x)$

22. **a.** Use an area model to find the factored form of the expression $x^2 + 7x + 12$.

   b. Use your answer to help you solve the equation $x^2 + 7x + 12 = 0$.

23. **a.** Use an area model to find the factored form of the expression $x^2 + 8x + 15$.

   b. Use your answer to help you solve the equation $x^2 + 8x + 15 = 0$.

24. **a.** Use an area model to find the factored form of the expression $x^2 - 9$.

   b. Use your answer to help you solve the equation $x^2 - 9 = 0$.

25. **a.** Use an area model to find the factored form of the expression $2x^2 + 5x + 3$.

   b. Use your answer to help you solve the equation $2x^2 + 5x + 3 = 0$.

In 26 and 27, solve the equation. Explain your reasoning.

26. $x^2 + 5x + 7 = 1$ **27.** $x^2 + 6x + 15 = 6$

---

20. $5 + 8(x + 2) = 6(1 + x) - 1$
$5 + 8x + 16 = 6 + 6x - 1$
$21 + 8x = 5 + 6x$
$16 + 8x = 6x$
$16 = {}^-2x$
$^-8 = x$

check: $5 + 8(^-8 + 2) = 6(1 + {}^-8) - 1$
$5 + 8(^-6) = 6(^-7) - 1$
$5 - 48 = {}^-42 - 1$
$^-43 = {}^-43$

21. $2x - 3(x + 4) - 10 = 9 - 3(2 + 2x)$
$2x - 3x - 12 - 10 = 9 - 6 - 6x$
$^-x - 22 = 3 - 6x$
$^-x = 25 - 6x$
$5x = 25$
$x = 5$

check: $2(5) - 3(5 + 4) - 10 = 9 - 3(2 + 10)$
$10 - 3(9) - 10 = 9 - 3(12)$
$^-27 = 9 - 36$
$^-27 = {}^-27$

19a. $(x + 2)(x - 1)(x - 5) = 0$ has solutions $x = {}^-2$, $x = 1$, and $x = 5$. Those are the points at which the graph crosses the x-axis.

19b. The values of x that satisfy $(x + 2)(x - 1)(x - 5) < 0$ are $x < {}^-2$ or $1 < x < 5$. These are the parts of the graph below the x-axis.

19c. Most students will use trial and error to answer this question by substituting a number that is less than 2 for x and seeing whether the result is positive or negative, and then repeating the process for a number between $^-2$ and 1, a number between 1 and 5, and a number greater than 5. A negative result in a given interval indicates that the x values in that interval satisfy the inequality.

20, 21. See below left.

22a. $x^2 + 7x + 12 = (x + 3)(x + 4)$

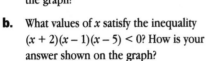

22b. The solutions to $(x + 3)(x + 4) = 0$ are $x = {}^-3$ and $x = {}^-4$.

23a. $x^2 + 8x + 15 = (x + 3)(x + 5)$

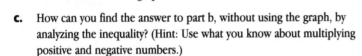

23b. The solutions to $(x + 3)(x + 5) = 0$ are $x = {}^-3$ and $x = {}^-5$.

24–27. See page 64r.

Mathematical Reflections

In this investigation, you learned methods for solving linear and quadratic equations. These questions will help you summarize what you have learned:

1 Describe some general strategies for solving linear equations. Give examples that illustrate your strategies.

2 **a.** What general strategies can you use to solve quadratic equations of the form $ax^2 + bx = 0$?

b. Will the strategies you described in part a work for solving quadratic equations of the form $ax^2 + bx + c = 0$? Use an example to help explain your answer.

3 In a–c, illustrate your ideas with an example.

a. How could you solve a linear equation of the form $mx + b = 0$ by using a graph?

b. How could you solve a linear equation of the form $ax + b = cx + d$ by using a graph?

c. How could you solve a quadratic equation of the form $ax^2 + bx = 0$ by using a graph?

Think about your answers to these questions, discuss your ideas with other students and your teacher, and then write a summary of your findings in your journal.

Tips for the Linguistically Diverse Classroom

Diagram Code The Diagram Code technique is described in detail in *Getting to Know Connected Mathematics*. Students use a minimal number of words and drawings, diagrams, or symbols to respond to questions that require writing. Example: Question 1—A student might respond to this question by writing the headings *Table, Graph,* and *Add/Subtract,* with an example under head heading.

TEACHING THE INVESTIGATION

4.1 • Comparing Costs

In this problem, students review their earlier mathematics work (from the grade 7 unit *Moving Straight Ahead*), solving equations of the form $ax + b = cx + d$ by finding the intersection of the graphs of $y = ax + b$ and $y = cx + d$ or the values in tables for which the y values are equal. In the next problem, they will solve an equation of the form $ax + b = cx + d$ symbolically.

Launch

Introduce the problem, and write the two bids on the board or display Transparency 4.1. Verify that students understand what the variables in the equations $y = 100 + 4x$ and $y = 25 + 7x$ represent.

> What kind of relationship does each equation represent? *(a linear relationship)*
>
> How do you know they are linear? *(because they can be rewritten in the form y = mx + b, which is the equation for a line)*
>
> What will the graphs of these equations look like? *(straight lines)*

As a review, you might ask more questions about rate of change and slope. Then ask:

> How can this information help us decide which bid to use if we are ordering a certain number of books?

Allow students to share their conjectures. Then have them work on the problem and the follow-up in groups of three or four.

Explore

As the problem is mostly review, this is an opportunity to observe what students recall about solving linear equations. In the grade 7 unit *Moving Straight Ahead*, students encountered and solved equations of the form $ax + b = cx + d$ by finding the intersection of the graphs of $y = ax + b$ and $y = cx + d$ and by locating the values in tables for which the y values are equal.

Summarize

Have several groups explain and demonstrate how they used the table and the graph to determine the number of books for which the bids are equal and for what numbers of books bid 1 is less than bid 2. A transparent grid showing the graphs will facilitate the discussion and also be useful for reviewing the follow-up.

Ask questions, such as those on the next page, to assess students' understanding of the relationship of the solution to an equation of the form $y = ax + b$ to a pair of values in the table, a point on the graph, and the two equations.

Find the cost of each bid for 10 books. *(bid 1, $140; bid 2, $95)*

How do the pairs of values (10, 140) and (10, 95) relate to the graphs of the equations? *(They each represent, or name, a point on a line.)*

How could you use a table to find these bids? *(find the y value that corresponds to 10 for each equation)*

How can you use a graph to find the cost for 20 books? How are these pairs of values related to the equations?

Discuss the follow-up questions. Question 1 reviews evaluating expressions for a particular value. Question 2 reviews solving a linear equation of the form $y = mx + b$. Students will likely solve this using tables or graphs, though some may use trial and error to substitute values of x in each equation until the value of y is as close to 300 as possible without exceeding it. Some may solve the equation symbolically. (In the grade 7 unit *Moving Straight Ahead,* students learned ways to solve linear equations of the form $y = mx + b$ without using tables or graphs.) This would be a good time to review a symbolic solution method. A discussion of solving the equations symbolically makes a nice transition into Problem 4.2; see the launch of that problem.

Review each of the methods that students suggest, and ask the class which method they think is the most efficient for solving such equations.

4.2 • Solving Linear Equations

In the previous problem, students reviewed how to use tables and graphs to solve linear equations. In this problem, they solve linear equations of the form $ax + b = cx + d$ using symbolic methods. Solutions that arise from symbolic methods are then connected to graphical and tabular solutions.

Launch

The discussion of question 2 from the follow-up of Problem 4.1 leads nicely into this launch.

In the follow-up to the last problem, you were asked this question: *For each bid, find the greatest number of books that can be printed if the cost is not to exceed $300.* How could you solve this by working with the equations?

Help students understand that they would substitute 300 for y in each bid equation and solve for the value of x. Write the equations on the board, and then substitute 300 for y.

Bid 1	**Bid 2**
$y = 100 + 4x$	$y = 25 + 7x$
$300 = 100 + 4x$	$300 = 25 + 7x$

Remind students of what they have learned in their earlier mathematics work.

To solve equations like these, you need to *undo* the mathematical operations until x is alone on one side of the equation. To make sure that the sides remain equal, you must apply any operations to *both* sides.

What might we do in each of these equations to try to isolate x on one side? For example, the bid $300 is obtained by adding $100 to the cost of the books, $4x$. So, you could subtract $100 from both sides.

As a class, solve both equations; one solution method for each is shown below. The symbolic method is also shown on Transparency 4.2A. Emphasize the idea of applying mathematical operations to both sides of an equation to keep the equation balanced.

Bid 1	**Bid 2**
$y = 100 + 4x$	$y = 25 + 7x$
$300 = 100 + 4x$	$300 = 25 + 7x$
$300 - 100 = 100 + 4x - 100$	$300 - 25 = 25 + 7x - 25$
$200 = 4x$	$275 = 7x$
$\frac{200}{4} = \frac{4x}{4}$	$\frac{275}{7} = \frac{7x}{7}$
$50 = x$	$39.3 \approx x$

With the solutions on the board, ask:

So, what do our answers tell us?

For bid 1, printing 50 books will cost exactly $300. For bid 2, 39 is the greatest number of books that can be printed for $300; the cost for 39 books is $25 + 7(39) = \$298$.

Next, introduce the idea of setting two equations equal to one another and finding a common solution. Write the equations representing bid 1 and bid 2 on the board again.

$$y = 100 + 4x \qquad\qquad y = 25 + 7x$$

Remember that these equations represent the bids from two printers. In the last problem, you used tables and graphs to find the number of books for which these two bids are equal.

Underneath the equations, write a third equation:

$$100 + 4x = 25 + 7x$$

What do you think *this* equation represents?

Help students to understand that solving this equation is another way to answer the question of for what number of books the bids will be equal. The left side represents the cost of bid 1; the right side represents the cost of bid 2. The equality says that the costs are equal. We need to find the value of x that will make the bids equal.

How would you solve this equation?

The symbolic method for solving this equation is the same: undo the mathematical operations until the variable is isolated on one side of the equation.

For the Teacher: Solving Equations Using a "Balance"

If students are finding the symbolic method of solving equations conceptually difficult, you might introduce the metaphor of a physical balance to help them grasp the concept of keeping an equation in balance.

When solving an equation, it may help to think of the sides of the equation as weights on opposite sides of a balance. For example, you can think of the equation $300 = 100 + 4x$ as follows:

> A bag containing 300 small beads exactly balances a bag containing 100 small beads and 4 large beads. Each small bead weighs 1 ounce. The weight of each large bead is unknown.

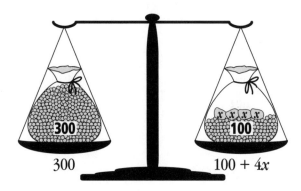

Solving $300 = 100 + 4x$ for x is equivalent to finding the weight of a large bead. You can find this weight by isolating a single large bead on one side while keeping the scale balanced.

Anytime you "perform an operation" on one side of the scale, you must perform the same operation on the other side to keep the scale balanced. For example:

$$300 = 100 + 4x$$
$$300 - 100 = 100 + 4x - 100 \quad \text{Remove 100 small beads from each side.}$$
$$200 = 4x$$
$$\frac{200}{4} = \frac{4x}{4}$$
$$50 = x$$

Divide the beads on each side into 4 equal groups, leaving one group on each side of the balance.

A pan balance can be used to demonstrate the operations: pennies could represent small beads and, in this case, bundles of 50 pennies (twisted in paper so students cannot see how many equal a large bead) could represent large beads. This adds authenticity to the method: when the last x bundle is opened, it is discovered to be the correct solution.

The balance metaphor may help students think about keeping the sides of the equation balanced, or equal, but it does have limitations. For example, it would be difficult to represent negative quantities or numbers other than whole numbers.

Have students work individually on the problem and then share their explanations for each step with a partner. Pairs can then answer the follow-up questions.

Explore

As students work, look for various first steps they use to solve the equation in a different way (part B). If they have trouble finding another way to solve the equation, ask:

> Besides $4x$, what else could you take from each side that would help you to eventually get x alone on one side?

If students have trouble with follow-up question 3, remind them that they did something similar in Problem 4.1. Challenge students who finish early to solve the equation by making a table and a graph. They can put the table and graph on blank transparencies or large sheets of paper and be prepared to explain their solutions.

Summarize

Have students share the various first steps they tried for solving the equation. In addition to subtracting $4x$ from both sides, there are three other logical first steps that will lead to a solution:

- subtracting 25 from both sides
- subtracting $7x$ from both sides
- subtracting 100 from both sides

Other first steps are mathematically valid but are inconvenient to execute or to no advantage. Discuss with the class the idea that any operation (except division by zero) can be applied to both sides, but that only some will easily lead to the desired solution. For example, adding 300 to both sides brings us no closer to a solution:

$$100 + 4x = 25 + 7x$$
$$100 + 300 + 4x = 25 + 300 + 7x$$
$$400 + 4x = 325 + 7x$$

Some students might try to divide both sides by 4 or by 7 to isolate an x on one side; however, this only makes the equation more complex. It is worth spending time analyzing the logic that makes this a possible, but not very convenient, move:

$$100 + 4x = 25 + 7x$$
$$\frac{100 + 4x}{4} = \frac{25 + 7x}{4}$$
$$25 + x = \frac{25}{4} + \frac{7x}{4}$$

The equation $25 + x = \frac{25}{4} + \frac{7x}{4}$ is logically equivalent to $100 + 4x = 25 + 7x$, but no easier to think about. Discussion of these subtleties will help students when they face more complex equations later.

Ask for answers to part C, and have the class evaluate each response. Be sure to discuss how to use the equation to answer the question.

> What does $x = 25$ imply about the equation $100 + 4x = 25 + 7x$?
> (If 25 is substituted for x, the sides of the equation are equal; they
> both equal 200.)

Discuss the follow-up questions. Question 3 asks how a graph and a table could be used to solve the equation $11x - 12 = 30 + 5x$. Use this opportunity to reinforce the idea that such equations can be solved by graphing two equations and finding the point of intersection. In this case, students would graph the equations $y = 11x - 12$ and $y = 30 + 5x$. If some students have prepared tables and graphs, let them share them with the class.

Ask students to compare the three methods—graphical, tabular, and symbolic—for solving linear equations and the advantages and disadvantages of each. At this point, students will have various ideas about the methods. They may mention the difficulty of finding an appropriate viewing window or adjusting the table settings when using a calculator. They may remark that one disadvantage of using equations is making mathematical errors.

To assess students' understanding of the symbolic solution method, have them solve another equation or two, such as the following:

$$5x + 17 = 2x + 50 \qquad\qquad 4x + 8 = 11 + 3x$$

4.3 • Reasoning with Symbols

Students continue to develop their ideas about symbolic solution strategies in this problem. Encouraging them to explain the logic of their arguments and to connect symbolic solutions to tabular and graphical solutions increases their proficiency with solving equations. They are also asked to look for general strategies, which will help them refine the symbolic solution technique.

Launch

Pose and have a short discussion about two or three examples, enough to focus students on the goals and reasoning of solving equations symbolically, rather than on specific mechanical steps.

> Think about the equation $3.1 = 2x + 11$. What is a *logical* first step for solving this equation symbolically? *(subtracting 11 from both sides)*

> What other first steps could you try? *(Students might mention several inefficient first steps, such as subtracting 3.1 from both sides, subtracting 2x from both sides, or dividing both sides by 2.)* Would these first steps be helpful? Which first step would you choose, and why?

Most students will select subtracting 11, but discuss the reasons for and against the other suggestions. You might follow through with them as well; for example:

$$
\begin{aligned}
3.1 &= 2x + 11 \\
0 &= 2x + 7.9 \\
{}^{-}7.9 &= 2x \\
\tfrac{{}^{-}7.9}{2} &= x \\
{}^{-}0.45 &= x
\end{aligned}
\qquad\qquad
\begin{aligned}
3.1 &= 2x + 11 \\
\tfrac{3.1}{2} &= x + \tfrac{11}{2} \\
\tfrac{3.1}{2} - \tfrac{11}{2} &= x \\
\tfrac{{}^{-}7.9}{2} &= x \\
{}^{-}0.45 &= x
\end{aligned}
$$

> What is a logical first step for solving the equation $3.1x = 2x + 11$? What are some other possible first steps?

Consider the equation $17x + 17 = x$. What first step seems logical? Why?

What is your ultimate goal when solving an equation using the symbolic method? *(to isolate the variable on one side of the equation)*

Explain that students will now practice solving more equations and that they should be prepared to explain why their solution strategies are sensible. Have them begin work on the problem individually and then compare methods in groups of two or three. When they finish, they can continue to work in groups on the follow-up questions.

Explore

Each of equations A–D can be solved in several logical ways. Students should explain their logic to the others in their groups and try to understand alternative solution methods. You might ask that each group choose the strategy that seems the most efficient for each equation and be ready to justify their choice to the class, but keep in mind that more than one strategy might be efficient.

If students have difficulty trying to define general strategies for solving linear equations in part F, ask if they see any similarities among the first steps they used in A–D. If they struggle with follow-up question 2, suggest that they start with the equation $x = 2$ and perform operations on both sides to create new equations. If time permits, ask each group to choose an equation from their work on question 2 and challenge other groups to verify that it has a solution of 2. The various examples could be displayed on a bulletin board.

Summarize

To review parts A–D, you might have each group choose one of the equations and explain the solution method that they feel is the most efficient. Then have them share the general strategies they found in part F. Some may suggest starting with the operation that seems to be the simplest numerically. Often this involves the undoing of addition and subtraction and then division. In other situations, particularly those involving parentheses, it may be best to do the multiplication first.

Use the discussion of follow-up question 1 to communicate the idea that there is an infinite number of (x, y) pairs that satisfy the equation $y = mx + b$ and that each pair of values represents a point on the graph of the equation.

Make sure the class understands that when a specific value of y is substituted into a general equation, such as $y = 7.5x - 23.5$, the solution to the equation is the corresponding value of x. Similarly, when a specific value of x is substituted into a general equation, the solution to the equation is the corresponding value of y. You might show an example of this as well; for instance, substituting $x = 0$ into the equation $y = 7.5x - 23.5$ gives a solution of $y = -23.5$.

Question 2 is an open-ended challenge; have students share the ways in which they approached writing an equation with a solution of $x = 2$. Some may have used trial and error; some may have started with the equation $x = 2$ and applied mathematical operations to both sides to create a new equation; for example:

$$x = 2$$
$$x + 7 = 2 + 7$$
$$x + 7 = 9$$
$$x + 7 + 2x = 9 + 2x$$
$$7 + 3x = 9 + 2x$$

$$x = 2$$
$$\frac{x}{2} = \frac{2}{2}$$
$$\frac{x}{2} = 1$$
$$\frac{x}{2} + 7 = 1 + 7$$
$$\frac{x}{2} + 7 = 8$$

Ask students to sketch graphs to show the solutions to the equations they wrote. Remind them of their work in Problems 4.1 and 4.2: finding the common solution to the equations $y = 100 + 4x$ and $y = 25 + 7x$ is the same as solving the equation $100 + 4x = 25 + 7x$.

For $7 + 3x = 9 + 2x$, for example, the graph would show the intersecting lines $y = 7 + 3x$ and $y = 9 + 2x$. For $\frac{x}{2} + 7 = 8$, the graph would show the intersecting lines $y = \frac{x}{2} + 7$ and $y = 8$.

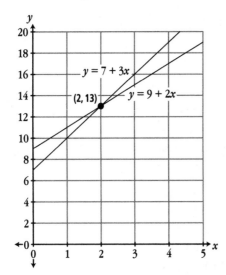
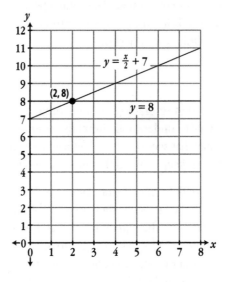

Infinitely many equations are equivalent to $x = 2$. The important idea is that the intersection point of the graphs related to each equation has an x-coordinate of 2 because each equation has the solution $x = 2$.

If time allows, have groups challenge each other by writing new linear equations and exchanging them. You can restrict equations to the form $ax + b = cx + d$, or you can allow any linear equations to surface. After the class has had time to explore, have them reflect on the general strategies for solving the equations by the symbolic method and on particular arrangements of symbols that may make one strategy easier than another.

> How do you know whether an equation is linear? Do you think you can use the symbolic method to solve *every* linear equation?
>
> Did anyone write an equation that contained parentheses? What strategies did you use to remove the parentheses?

Ask whether some of the equations may have been easier to solve using a graphing calculator (some of the equations in the follow-up, for example, may be easier to solve using a calculator).

Offer this equation to assist students' understanding (linear equations with fractions have not been discussed much, so you may choose to write the equation without fractions):

$$2(x + 3) - \frac{x}{3} = \frac{6x + 3}{5} - 2$$

Let some students solve this symbolically and others solve it graphically. Discuss the pros and cons of each solution method.

4.4 • **Solving Quadratic Equations**

In this problem, students learn that the factored form of a quadratic equation is more convenient than the expanded form for finding the solutions of that equation. Students are then encouraged to make the connection between the solution of a quadratic equation and the x-intercepts of the graph of that equation.

Launch

The method of solving a quadratic equation by factoring is based on an important property of real numbers: if a and b are real numbers and $ab = 0$, then a, b, or both must be equal to 0. Generally, knowing the result of a product of factors is of no help in determining the factors themselves. For example, if we know that the product of two numbers is 12, we have an infinite number of choices for the numbers (3×4, 2×6, $^-2 \times {^-6}$, 24×0.5, and so on). However, if the product is 0, we know that one or both of the factors must be equal to 0.

Use the following exercise to help students reach their own understanding of this idea. First, choose two numbers with a product of 12, such as $\frac{5}{2}$ and $\frac{24}{5}$, that would be difficult to guess.

> I am thinking of two numbers whose product is 12. Can you guess my numbers? *(Say no to each of their incorrect guesses.)*

When students realize that they can't guess your numbers or that it would take many guesses, ask a fairer question.

> I am thinking of two numbers whose product is 0. Can you guess my numbers?

This time, students will be partially successful: they will realize that one of the numbers must be 0.

> I am thinking of two other numbers whose product is 0. One of the numbers is 5 more than the other. Can you guess my numbers?

Students should reason that one of the numbers must be 0 and that the other must be 5 more or 5 less than 0.

> So, if the product of my two numbers is 0, what do you know about at least one of the two numbers? *(At least one of the two numbers must be 0.)*

> How can we write this product using symbols? *[x(x + 5) = 0]*

Explain that in this problem, students will be using the idea of products being equal to 0 to solve quadratic equations. Write the equation $y = x(x + 5)$ on the board, and then rewrite it in expanded form, $y = x^2 + 5x$.

> What kind of equation is this? *(a quadratic equation)*

> What does the graph of this equation look like? *(It is a parabola that opens upward.)*

Explain that finding the x-intercepts of the graph of $y = x^2 + 5x$ is the same as solving the equation $x^2 + 5x = 0$.

> You know that you can solve a linear equation like $2x + 3 = 0$ by graphing the equation and seeing where the line crosses the x-axis. In the same way, solving a quadratic equation is equivalent to finding where its graph crosses the x-axis. In other words, you can solve a quadratic equation like $x^2 + 5x = 0$ by finding the x-intercepts.
>
> The x-intercepts are the points on the graph that represent the solutions when $y = 0$. The x-intercepts are also called the *roots* of a quadratic equation.
>
> In this problem, you will develop methods for finding the roots of a quadratic equation by working with the symbols rather than by making a table or a graph.

Have students work in pairs on the problem and the follow-up.

Explore

Students may have trouble grasping the connection between writing a quadratic expression in factored form and finding the x-intercepts of the corresponding graph. If so, remind them of the exercise from the launch.

> You have found the two factors of $x^2 + 3x$. What must be true for the product of these two factors to be 0? *(One or both of the factors must be equal to 0.)*
>
> Let's look at one of the factors, $x + 3$. What must be true for this factor to be equal to 0? *(The value of x must be ⁻3.)*

Some students may be able to look at the equation $x^2 + 3x = 0$, recognize that $x = 0$ is one solution, and find that $x = {}^-3$ is the other solution by trial and error. This method is fine, but encourage them to use the factored form to find the solutions so that they will be able to solve more difficult equations later. If necessary, remind them to set each linear factor equal to 0 and then solve the linear equations, $x = 0$ and $x + 3 = 0$.

In the equations in part E, the coefficient of x^2 is something other than 1. If students are finding this fairly easy, you might give them other equations to solve; for example:

$$y = 15x - 3x^2 \qquad y = 20x - 15x^2 \qquad y = 6x^2 - 14x \qquad y = 18x - 27x^2$$

Students can find the factored form of each equation and then set each linear factor equal to 0 to solve it.

Question 4 of the follow-up presents an expression in the form $ax^2 + bx + c$. Students do not yet know how to factor such expressions using the distributive property, but they can apply an area model to determine the factors. You might challenge students who finish early with other equations of the form $ax^2 + bx + c = 0$ to factor; for example:

$$x^2 + 8x + 16 = 0 \qquad x^2 + x - 6 = 0 \qquad 2x^2 + 7x + 6 = 0$$

Summarize

Discuss the strategies that students used to find the solution to each equation in the problem. They should explain that they worked from the factored form by finding when each factor is 0. Many students will be able to determine when each factor is 0 by inspection, but for factors such as $2x + 1$, as in follow-up question 3, they may need to solve the related equation, $2x + 1 = 0$.

Spend some time discussing question 4 of the follow-up. Students probably can't factor the equation $x^2 + 8x + 12 = 0$ using the distributive property because the three terms do not have a common factor. However, they do know how to factor such trinomials using an area model.

> In question 4, you used an area model to factor the expression. Why couldn't you have just removed a common factor from each term? *(because there is no factor that is common to all three terms)*
>
> Instead, you used an area model. What did this accomplish? *(This helped us to figure out what the factors were.)*
>
> Describe some other quadratic equations that can be solved using an area model.

Most of the quadratic equations that students have worked with can be solved using an area model, but factoring equations symbolically is sometimes possible and quicker. In fact, area models are sometimes difficult to use when the equations involve negative signs.

Next, help students extend their understanding by presenting a few equations in slightly different forms.

> How could you solve $x^2 = {}^-7x$?

If students don't have any ideas about how to approach this, ask:

> Could you rewrite this equation to get it into a form that you *do* know how to solve? *[Yes; it is equivalent to $x^2 + 7x = 0$, which is easy to factor: $x(x + 7) = 0$, so the solutions are $x = 0$ and $x = {}^-7$.]*
>
> How could you solve $x^2 - 7x = {}^-12$?

The 12 can be moved to the left side of the equation, and then $x^2 - 7x + 12 = 0$ can be factored, using an area model, to $(x - 4)(x - 3) = 0$; the solutions are thus $x = 3$ and $x = 4$. ACE questions 26 and 27 offer students more practice with this idea.

> Can you use factoring to solve $x^2 + 2 = 0$?

Let students share any ideas they have. Ask questions to guide their thinking.

> Can you factor out an x from $x^2 + 2$? *(No, because the second term does not contain an x.)*
>
> Can you make an area model to help you factor $x^2 + 2$? *(Students may need to attempt this before they realize that it is not possible.)*

What does the graph of $y = x^2 + 2$ look like? *(It is a parabola that does not cross the x-axis.)*

What does this mean? *(This means y never equals 0.)*

Look again at the equation. Does it make sense that y can never equal 0? *(Yes, because x^2 can never be less than 0, so y can never be less than 2. This means the equation $y = x^2 + 2$ has no solutions!)*

Try $x^2 + 5 = 0$ and $x^2 + 9 = 0$. Are the results the same? *(yes)*

To help students see this, give them some other equations that cannot be solved this way, such as $x^2 + 1 = 0$ and $x^2 + 10x - 10 = 0$. Let them use their graphing calculators to confirm their answers. Students may see that equations of the form $ax^2 + bx = 0$ can be solved by factoring, but that those of the form $ax^2 + bx + c = 0$ are not as easy to solve.

For the Teacher: The Quadratic Formula

Most quadratic equations are not as readily factored as those in this problem. The quadratic formula can be used to find the solutions to any quadratic equation. The solutions to a quadratic equation of the form $y = ax^2 + bx + c$ are given by the quadratic formula:

$$x = \frac{-b \pm \sqrt{b^2 - 4ac}}{2a}$$

For example, applying the quadratic formula to the equation $y = x^2 + 10x - 10$ yields the following:

$$x = \frac{-10 \pm \sqrt{10^2 - 4(1)(-10)}}{2(1)}$$

$$x = \frac{-10 \pm \sqrt{140}}{2}$$

$$x \approx -10.92 \text{ or } 0.92$$

This is beyond the scope of this course, but you might tell students that in later courses they will learn a way to solve *any* quadratic equation or to discover that the quadratic equation has no solution.

To assess what students have learned, present several more equations for them to solve, such as the following:

- $x^2 - 13.4x = 0$ (This emphasizes that solutions can be non–whole numbers.)

- $2.3x^2 - 13.4x = 0$

- $2.3x^2 - 2.3x = 0$

- $x + 10x^2 = 0$ (Students who are looking for shortcuts may find $x = -10$ rather than $\frac{-1}{10}$.)

- $x^2 = 10x$

- $x^2 + 4 = 0$ (This equation has no solutions.)

- $x^2 - 4 = 0$

Have students enter the equations on the overhead graphing calculator, if one is available, and set an appropriate graphing window. The graphical and tabular methods can be used to confirm the results of the symbolic method.

End the exploration by asking students:

> Do you think you will *always* be able to solve a quadratic equation by factoring it? *(no)*
>
> If you can't solve a quadratic equation by factoring it, what can you do? *(You can make a table or a graph.)*

Leave students with this idea:

> You won't always be able to factor equations like these. Remember, though, if you can't figure out how to solve an equation by factoring it, you can always make a graph or a table to solve it.

Additional Answers

Answers to Problem 4.1

B. The point of intersection, (25, 200), lies on both graphs, so the values $x = 25$ and $y = 200$ satisfy both equations and the bids are the same for 25 books.

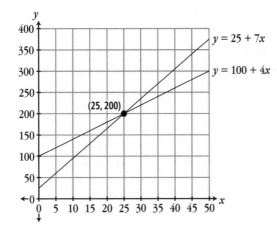

C. For 25 books, the bids are equal. The graph shows that for more than 25 books, bid 1 is less than bid 2 because the graph for bid 1 is lower than the graph for bid 2. For example, if the number of books is 26, bid 1 is $204 and bid 2 is $207. Since bid 2 increases more with each book, if the number of books is greater than 25, bid 1 is lower.

Answers to Problem 4.2

B. Possible answer:

$$100 + 4x = 25 + 7x$$
$$100 + 4x - 25 = 25 + 7x - 25$$
$$75 + 4x = 7x$$
$$75 + 4x - 4x = 7x - 4x$$
$$75 = 3x$$
$$\frac{75}{3} = \frac{3x}{3}$$
$$25 = x$$

C. You can check the solution by substituting 25 for x in the original equation to see whether it produces an equality:

$$100 + 4(25) = 25 + 7(25)$$
$$100 + 100 = 25 + 175$$
$$200 = 200$$

(Note: If students do not use a symbolic method to check this solution, demonstrate the method in the summary of the problem.)

Answers to Problem 4.2 Follow-Up

1. Possible answer:

$$11x - 12 = 30 + 5x$$

$11x - 12 + 12 = 30 + 5x + 12$ Add 12 to both sides.

$$11x = 42 + 5x$$

$11x - 5x = 42 + 5x - 5x$ Subtract 5x from both sides.

$$6x = 42$$

$\frac{6x}{6} = \frac{42}{6}$ Divide both sides by 6.

$$x = 7$$

2. You can check by substituting 7 for x in the original equation to see whether it produces an equality. (Note: Students might also use a table or a graph.)

$$11(7) - 12 = 30 + 5(7)$$
$$77 - 12 = 30 + 35$$
$$65 = 65$$

3. To solve the equation, graph $y = 11x - 12$ and $y = 30 + 5x$ on the same set of axes. The solution will be the x-coordinate of the point of intersection. Or, make a table for the equations $y = 11x - 12$ and $y = 30 + 5x$. The solution will be the x value for which the two y values are equal. The x-coordinate of the point of intersection, the x value for which the two y values are equal, and the value of x found in the symbolic solution will all be the same.

Answers to Problem 4.3

A possible solution is offered for each of parts A–D. Note: Some students will be able to do more than one step at a time (as done below), which is fine for students who catch on quickly. Caution students who make a lot of mistakes to slow down and show each step.

A.
$$7x + 15 = 12x + 5$$
$$15 = 5x + 5$$
$$10 = 5x$$
$$2 = x$$

B.
$$14 - 3x = 1.5x + 5$$
$$14 = 4.5x + 5$$
$$9 = 4.5x$$
$$2 = x$$

C.
$$-3x + 5 = 2x - 10$$
$$5 = 5x - 10$$
$$15 = 5x$$
$$3 = x$$

D.
$$3 + 5(x + 2) = 7x - 1$$
$$3 + 5x + 10 = 7x - 1$$
$$5x + 14 = 7x$$
$$14 = 2x$$
$$7 = x$$

E.
$$7x + 15 = 12x + 5$$
$$7(2) + 15 = 12(2) + 5$$
$$14 + 15 = 24 + 5$$
$$29 = 29$$

$$14 - 3x = 1.5x + 5$$
$$14 - 3(2) = 1.5(2) + 5$$
$$14 - 6 = 3 + 5$$
$$8 = 8$$

$$-3x + 5 = 2x - 10$$
$$-3(3) + 5 = 2(3) - 10$$
$$-9 + 5 = 6 - 10$$
$$-4 = -4$$

$$3 + 5(x + 2) = 7x - 1$$
$$3 + 5(7 + 2) = 7(7) - 1$$
$$3 + 45 = 49 - 1$$
$$48 = 48$$

Answers to Problem 4.3 Follow-Up

1. A table and a graph are shown for each equation.

   a. This equation was written for finding the value of x when $y = 51.5$, which is $x = 10$. A graph and a table are both useful, though students will probably use a table.

x	$y = 7.5x - 23.5$
6	21.5
7	29
8	36.5
9	44
10	51.5
11	59

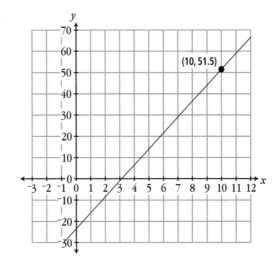

b. This equation was written for finding the value of x when $y = 0$ (in other words, the x-intercept), which is $x = 3\frac{2}{15}$ or about 3.13. The graph and the table are both useful, though it may be difficult for students to find the exact answer.

x	$y = 7.5x - 23.5$
3.0	−1.00
3.1	−0.25
3.2	0.50
3.3	1.25
3.4	2.00
3.5	2.75

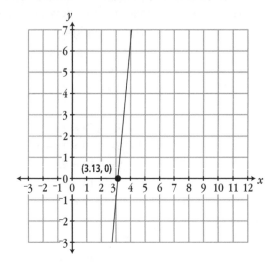

c. This equation was written for finding the value of x when $y = {}^{-}30$, which is approximately $^{-}0.867$. Neither the table nor the graph will give an exact answer, though students can zoom in on either to find more accurate answers.

x	$y = 7.5x - 23.5$
−1.10	−31.75
−1.05	−31.38
−1.00	−31.00
−0.95	−30.63
−0.90	−30.25
−0.85	−29.88

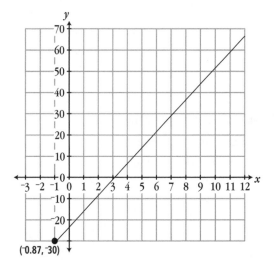

2. Answers will vary. It is highly unlikely that everyone wrote the same equation. Some possibilities: $2x = 4$, $3x + 5 = x + 9$, $13 = 2(x + 4) + 1$, $\frac{2x + 4}{2} = 4$

3. a. Set the equation equal to 200, and solve for x.

   $200 = 3x - (100 + 2x)$
   $200 = 3x - 100 - 2x$
   $200 = x - 100$
   $300 = x$ The choir must sell 300 boxes to make a $200 profit.

   b. The break-even point is when profit is equal to 0. Set the equation equal to 0, and solve for x.

   $0 = 3x - (100 + 2x)$
   $0 = 3x - 100 - 2x$
   $0 = x - 100$
   $100 = x$ The choir must sell 100 boxes to break even.

Answers to Problem 4.4

E. In each case, the factored form is more convenient for finding the roots of the equation.

1. For $4x(x - 2)$ to equal 0, one or both of the factors must equal 0: $4x = 0$ or $x - 2 = 0$. Thus, $x = 0$ or $x = 2$.

2. For $6x(5 - 2x)$ to equal 0, one or both of the factors must equal 0: $6x = 0$ or $5 - 2x = 0$. Thus, $x = 0$ or $x = \frac{5}{2}$.

F.
1. $x^2 + 4.5x = 0$
$x(x + 4.5) = 0$
$x = 0$ or $x = {}^-4.5$

2. $x^2 - 9x = 0$
$x(x - 9) = 0$
$x = 0$ or $x = 9$

3. ${}^-x^2 + 10x = 0$
$x({}^-x + 10) = 0$
$x = 0$ or $x = 10$

Answers to Problem 4.4 Follow-Up

1. Substitute the values of x into each equation.

$x^2 + 4.5x = 0$ $\qquad$ $x^2 + 4.5x = 0$
$0^2 + 4.5(0) = 0$ $\qquad$ $({}^-4.5)^2 + 4.5({}^-4.5) = 0$
$0 + 0 = 0$ $\qquad\qquad$ $({}^-4.5)^2 - 4.5^2 = 0$
$\qquad\qquad\qquad\qquad$ $20.25 - 20.25 = 0$

$x^2 - 9x = 0$ $\qquad$ $x^2 - 9x = 0$
$0^2 - 9(0) = 0$ $\qquad$ $9^2 - 9(9) = 0$
$0 = 0$ $\qquad\qquad\quad$ $81 - 81 = 0$

${}^-x^2 + 10x = 0$ $\qquad$ ${}^-x^2 + 10x = 0$
${}^-0^2 + 10(0) = 0$ $\qquad$ ${}^-10^2 + 10(10) = 0$
$0 = 0$ $\qquad\qquad\quad$ ${}^-100 + 100 = 0$

2. $x^2 + 4.5x$

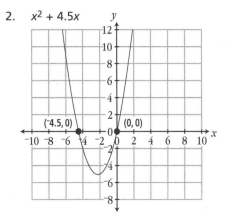

3. a. i. $(2x + 1)(x + 5) = 2x^2 + 11x + 5$

ii. $(x + 2)(x - 2) = x^2 - 4$

b. The factored form is more useful for predicting the x-intercepts.
If $(2x + 1)(x + 5) = 0$, then $2x + 1 = 0$ or $x + 5 = 0$. Thus, $x = {}^-\frac{1}{2}$ or $x = {}^-5$.
If $(x + 2)(x - 2) = 0$, then $x + 2 = 0$ or $x - 2 = 0$. Thus, $x = {}^-2$ or $x = 2$.

$y = x^2 - 9x$

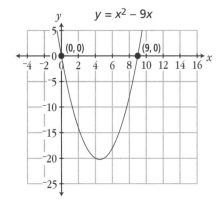

4. The area model shows that the factors of $x^2 + 8x + 12$ are $x + 6$ and $x + 2$. The solutions to the equation $x^2 + 8x + 12 = 0$, or $(x + 2)(x + 6) = 0$, are thus $x = {}^-2$ or $x = {}^-6$.

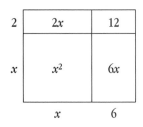

2	2x	12
x	x^2	6x
	x	6

$y = {}^-x^2 + 10x$

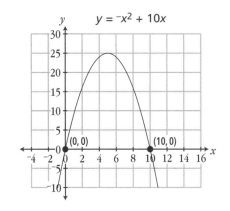

ACE Answers

Applications

5.
$$8.3x - 10.75 = 51.5$$
$$8.3x - 10.75 + 10.75 = 51.5 + 10.75$$
$$8.3x = 62.25$$
$$\frac{8.3x}{8.3} = \frac{62.25}{8.3}$$
$$x = 7.5$$

6. $x = 0$ or $x = 7$

7.
$$x^2 + 1.5x = 0$$
$$x(x + 1.5) = 0$$
$$x = 0 \text{ or } x = {}^-1.5$$

8.
$$x^2 + 6x + 8 = 0$$
$$(x + 2)(x + 4) = 0$$
$$x = {}^-2 \text{ or } x = {}^-4$$

9.
$$x^2 + 2x + 1 = 0$$
$$(x + 1)(x + 1) = 0$$
$$x = {}^-1$$

10.
$$8x - x^2 = 0$$
$$x(8 - x) = 0$$
$$x = 0 \text{ or } x = 8$$

24a. $x^2 - 3x + 3x - 9 = x^2 - 9 = (x - 3)(x + 3)$

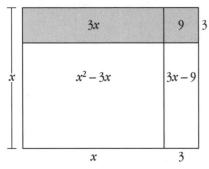

24b. The solutions to $(x - 3)(x + 3) = 0$ are $x = 3$ and $x = {}^-3$.

25a. $2x^2 + 5x + 3 = (2x + 3)(x + 1)$

1	2x	3
x	2x²	3x
	2x	3

25b. The solutions to $(2x + 3)(x + 1) = 0$ are $x = \frac{{}^-3}{2}$ and $x = {}^-1$.

26. Students may use an area model to factor the equation.
$$x^2 + 5x + 7 = 1$$
$$x^2 + 5x + 7 - 1 = 1 - 1$$
$$x^2 + 5x + 6 = 0$$
$$(x + 2)(x + 3) = 0$$
$$x = {}^-2 \text{ or } x = {}^-3$$

27. Students may use an area model to factor the equation.
$$x^2 + 6x + 15 = 6$$
$$x^2 + 6x + 15 - 6 = 6 - 6$$
$$x^2 + 6x + 9 = 0$$
$$(x + 3)(x + 3) = 0$$
$$x = {}^-3$$

Mathematical Reflections

1. Linear equations can be solved by making tables or graphs or solving the equation to get x on one side and a constant on the other. The goal is to undo the operations on either side of the equation, by adding, subtracting, multiplying, and dividing on both sides, keeping the equation balanced. Some choices for proceeding are more helpful than others. Adding and subtracting first often, but not always, leads to a simpler equation. Division first is not a helpful first step if it results in a more complicated expression. For example, to solve the equation $x + 7 = 2x + 5$, you can make a table to find the value of x for which the expressions on either side are equal, you can graph the two related equations, or you can solve the equation symbolically.

x	$x + 7$	$2x + 5$
0	7	5
1	8	7
2	9	9
3	10	11
4	11	13

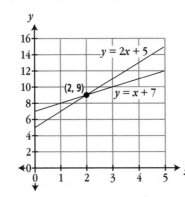

$$x + 7 = 2x + 5$$
$$x + 7 - 5 = 2x + 5 - 5$$
$$x + 2 = 2x$$
$$x + 2 - x = 2x - x$$
$$2 = x$$

2a. You can make a table to find the points where y is 0. You can graph the equation and look for the x-intercepts. Or you can try to factor the equation, maybe using an area model and find the values of x that make each factor equal to 0.

2b. You can still make a table and a graph of this form of quadratic equation. You might be able to factor it by drawing an area model and then setting each factor equal to 0. For example, for $x^2 + 5x + 6 = 0$, an area model can help you factor the expression to obtain $(x + 3)(x + 2) = 0$, so the solutions are $x = {}^-3$ and $x = {}^-2$.

3a. To solve an equation of the form $mx + b = 0$, graph the related equation and find the point where the graph crosses the x-axis. To solve $2x - 8 = 0$, graph $y = 2x - 8$. This crosses the x-axis at $x = 4$, so this is the solution.

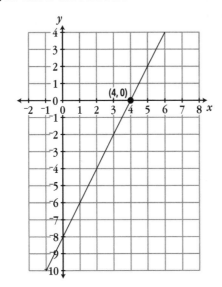

3b. The solution to an equation of the form $ax + b = cx + d$ will be the x-coordinate of the point where $y = ax + b$ intersects $y = cx + d$. To solve $3x - 5 = x + 1$, graph $y = 3x - 5$ and $y = x + 1$. They intersect at $(3, 4)$, so $x = 3$ is the solution.

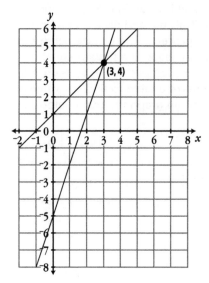

3c. The solution to an equation of the form $ax^2 + bx = 0$ will be the x-coordinates of the points where the graph of $y = ax^2 + bx$ crosses the x-axis, or where $y = 0$. To solve $x^2 + 4x = 0$, graph $y = x^2 + 4x$. It intersects the x-axis at $x = 0$ and $x = ^-4$, so these are the solutions.

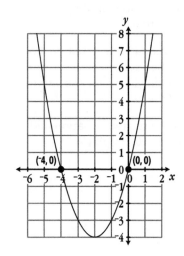

Writing Expressions for Surface Area

In this investigation, students will encounter a problem that can be approached in several ways. The various ways of thinking about the problem will lead to different, but equivalent, expressions for modeling the data. Each expression will represent a pattern that a particular student or group of students saw in the data or reflect the logic that was applied to the situation. Students can verify that the expressions are equivalent by using tables and graphs, by validating the underlying logic represented by the expressions, and by applying the properties of real numbers.

The activity that leads to the various expressions is presented in Problem 5.1, Stacking Rods. In this activity, students are asked to find an expression for the surface area of a staggered stack of *N* rods of a particular length.

After students have shared their various expressions, they can look for a pattern among them and, optionally, develop an equation for the surface area of a staggered stack of rods of any length.

Mathematical and Problem-Solving Goals

- **To find and compare equivalent expressions in a given context**

- **To evaluate expressions for a specific value of a variable**

Materials

Problem	For students	For the teacher
5.1	Graphing calculators, Cuisenaire rods (4 to 6 of the same color rod plus 3 or 4 unit rods per pair of students), centimeter rulers (optional), large sheets of paper (1 per pair)	Transparency 5.1, overhead graphing calculator, Cuisenaire rods for the overhead (all optional)

INVESTIGATION 5

Writing Expressions for Surface Area

In this unit, you have seen that many situations can be represented by several different, but equivalent, algebraic expressions, and you have learned methods for writing equivalent expressions. You have also developed algebraic strategies for solving linear and quadratic equations. In this investigation, you will apply all the ideas you have learned.

5.1 Stacking Rods

In this problem, you will find the surface area of stacks of staggered rods.

Problem 5.1

You will need four to six rods of the same length and several unit rods. In this problem, you will find the surface area of stacks of the longer rods. The rods in each stack should be staggered by 1 unit, as shown below.

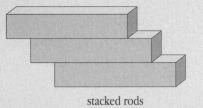

stacked rods   unit rod

A. Use the unit rods to determine the dimensions of one of the longer rods.

B. Find the surface area of a single rod, a stack of two rods, a stack of three rods, and so on.

C. Use your findings to help you write an equation for the relationship between the surface area, A, and the number of rods in the stack, N.

Answers to Problem 5.1

A. The lengths of the rods are as follows: red, 2; light green, 3; purple, 4; yellow, 5; dark green, 6; black, 7; brown, 8; blue, 9; orange, 10. The other two dimensions of each rod are both 1 unit.

B. See the tables in the "Summarize" section, which show the surface areas for stacks of rods from length 2 to length 10. At right are the results for rods of length 4.

C. For rods of length 4, a possible equation is $A = 18 + 12(N - 1)$. See the "Summarize" section for other possible equations.

Length 4

Number of rods	Surface area
1	18
2	30
3	42
4	54

At a Glance

Grouping:
pairs

Launch

- Introduce the idea of finding the surface area of a staggered stack of rods.

- Demonstrate how to measure with a unit cube.

- Have pairs explore the problem and follow-up.

Explore

- Help students who are having trouble seeing a pattern in their calculations.

Summarize

- Ask students to share their equations and strategies for each length.

- As a class, verify the equivalence of the expressions for each length.

- Pose the challenge of finding a general equation for any length. *(optional)*

Assignment Choices

ACE questions 1–6 and unassigned choices from earlier problems

Problem 5.1 Follow-Up

1. Compare your expression for surface area with the expressions written by other groups who used rods of the same length.
   a. Are all the expressions equivalent? Explain why or why not by using the rules you have learned for writing equivalent expressions.
   b. Use your calculator to make a table and a graph of your equation. How could you use tables or graphs to check whether the expressions found by your group and the other groups are equivalent?

2. a. Use your equation to find the surface area of a stack of 12 rods.
   b. Use your equation to find the surface area of a stack of 20 rods.

3. Will your equation work to calculate the surface area of stacks made from rods of a different length? If not, how could you change your equation so it would work? Check your idea by looking at the equations written by groups who used rods of a different length.

4. Is the relationship between the surface area and the number of rods linear, quadratic, exponential, or none of these? Explain your answer.

Answers to Problem 5.1 Follow-Up

All answers are given for rods of length 4.

1. See page 70f.

2. a. $A = 12(12) + 6 = 150$ square units   b. $A = 12(20) + 6 = 246$ square units

3. The same reasoning used to develop the equation would apply to different lengths, but would yield different equations. For example, in the equation $A = 2[4(N + 1) + N] + 2(N - 1)$, the 4 represents the length of a rod. This equation could be adapted to yield equations for rods of different lengths.

4. The relationship is linear. Explanations will vary. The equation $A = 12N + 6$ has the form of a linear equation. The variable N is raised to the first power. Its graph is a straight line and shows a constant rate of change between the variables N and A: as N increases by 1, A increases by 6.

Applications • Connections • Extensions

As you work on these ACE questions, use your calculator whenever you need it.

Applications

1. In their work in Problem 5.1, Kwang-Hee's group used rods that are 4 units long. They wrote this equation for the surface area of a stack of N rods:

$$A = 18 + 12(N - 1)$$

   a. Is this equation correct? Explain how you know.

   b. What is the surface area of a stack of 15 of these rods?

   c. If the surface area of a stack of these rods is 246 square units, how many rods are in the stack? Explain how you found your answer.

2. In their work in Problem 5.1, two groups in Mr. Samartino's class used rods that are 4 units long. Each group wrote an equation for the surface area of a stack of N rods.

$$A = 18 + 12(N - 1)$$

$$A = 4(2N + 2) + 2(2N - 1)(1)$$

   a. For each equation, describe how the group might have thought about the problem. Explain what each part of the equation represents.

   b. Show that the expressions for the surface area are equivalent.

   c. The surface area of a particular stack of these rods is 258 square units. Use one of the equations to find the number of rods in the stack. Check your answer by substituting the values for A and N into both equations.

2a. The equation $A = 18 + 12(N - 1)$ can be derived as explained in the answer to question 1a. The equation $A = 4(2N + 2) + 2(2N - 1)(1)$ can be derived by thinking of the stack as having N surfaces in front and back and one surface on the top and the bottom, or $2N + 2$ surfaces, which must be multiplied by 4 for the length, giving $4(2N + 2)$ for that part of the surface area. Then there are two "staircases," one on either end, each having $2N - 1$ surfaces, which adds $2(2N - 1)(1)$ to the area expression.

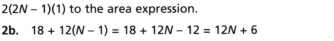
←— staircase

2b. $18 + 12(N - 1) = 18 + 12N - 12 = 12N + 6$

$4(2N + 2) + 2(2N - 1)(1) = 8N + 8 + 4N - 2 = 12N + 6$

Answers

Applications

1a. The equation is correct. Possible explanation: The equation can be derived by noting that the area increases by 12 for each additional rod after the first. The surface area is thus $18 + 12 + 12 + 12 + \cdots$, in which the number of 12s added is one less than the number of rods. Or, the table shows that this is a linear relationship with equation $A = 12N + 6$, which is equivalent to Kwang-Hee's equation: $A = 18 + 12(N - 1) = 18 + 12N - 12 = 12N + 6$.

Number of rods	Surface area
1	18
2	30
3	42
4	54

1b. $A = 18 + 12(N - 1) = 18 + 12(15 - 1) = 18 + 12(14) = 186$ square units

1c. $246 = 18 + 12(N - 1)$
$246 = 18 + 12N - 12$
$246 = 12N + 6$
$240 = 12N$
$20 = N$
The stack contains 20 rods.

2a, b. See below left.

2c. See page 70g.

3a. Answers will vary, even if students think about the problem as directed. The prism is 4 units long, N units high, and 1 unit wide. The front and back surfaces each have an area of $4N$, the top and bottom surfaces each have an area of $4(1) = 4$, and the sides each have an area of $N(1) = N$. The prism's surface area is thus $2(4N + 4 + N)$. This prism has less surface area than the original stack because the "stairs" have been eliminated. Each stair adds an area of 1. There are $N - 1$ stairs on each side, for an additional surface area of $2(N - 1)$. This leads to the expression $2(4N + 4 + N) + 2(N - 1)$.

3b. As shown in the answer to 2b, each expression in question 2 is equivalent to $12N + 6$. This expression is as well:
$2(4N + 4 + N) + 2(N - 1) = 10N + 8 + 2N - 2 = 12N + 6$.

Connections

4. See below right.

---

3. In Problem 5.1, Brianna worked with rods that are 4 units long. To find the surface area of each stack, she slid the rods into a rectangular prism. She found the surface area of the prism and then added the extra area created by staggering the rods.

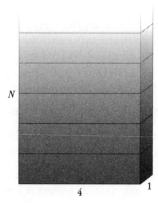

a. Write an expression for surface area that represents Brianna's method.

b. Show that your expression from part a is equivalent to the expressions in ACE question 2.

Connections

4. a. Write an equation for the surface area of a stack of N staggered rods if each rod is 12 units long.

b. If the surface area of a particular stack of these rods is 162 square units, how many rods are in the stack?

c. Write an equation for the volume of a stack of N of these rods.

4a. Answers will vary; students may have several approaches for writing an equation. For example, for a rod of length 4, an equation is $A = 2[4(N + 1) + N] + 2(N - 1)$. The 4 represents the length of the rod. For rods of length 12, some equations are thus $A = 2[12(N + 1) + N] + 2(N - 1)$, $A = 2(13N + 12) + 2N - 2$, and $A = 28N + 22$.

4b.
$$A = 28N + 22$$
$$162 = 28N + 22$$
$$140 = 28N$$
$$5 = N \qquad \text{There are 5 rods in the stack.}$$

4c. volume $= 12(N)(1) = 12N$

Extensions

5. Consider rods of length 1, 2, 3, 4, 5, 6, 7, 8, 9, and 10 units.

   a. Make a table showing the surface area of a stack of N staggered rods of each length.

Length of rod	Surface area of a stack of N rods
1	
2	
3	

   b. Describe any patterns in your table.

   c. Write an equation for the surface area, A, of a stack of N rods of length L.

6. Rods of length 4 units are stacked to form a rectangular prism.

   a. What are the dimensions of the prism?

   b. Write an equation for the surface area, A, of the prism.

   c. What is the surface area of a prism 10 rods high and 10 rods wide?

   d. Is the relationship between the surface area and the number of rods linear, quadratic, exponential, or none of these? Explain your answer.

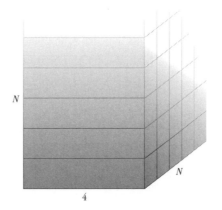

5a.

Length of rod	Surface area of a stack of N rods
1	$6N$
2	$8N + 2$
3	$10N + 4$
4	$12N + 6$
5	$14N + 8$
6	$16N + 10$
7	$18N + 12$
8	$20N + 14$
9	$22N + 16$
10	$24N + 18$

(Note: Although it is not really possible to make a staggered stack of unit rods, the pattern still holds.)

5b. For each increase of 1 in the length, surface area increases by $2N + 2$.

5a, b. See below left.

5c. Possible equations:
$A = 6N + (2N + 2)(L - 1)$,
$A = (2L + 4)N + 2L - 2$, or
$A = 2N(L + 2) + 2(L - 1)$

Rather than starting from scratch for each length rod, students might adapt the strategy used for a particular length; for example, by replacing the 4 that represents rod length in the equation $A = 2[4(N + 1) + 1(N)] + 2(N - 1)$, we obtain:

■ $A = 2[1(N + 1) + 1(N)] + 2(N - 1)$ for rods of length 1

■ $A = 2[3(N + 1) + 1(N)] + 2(N - 1)$ for rods of length 3

■ $A = 2[5(N + 1) + 1(N)] + 2(N - 1)$ for rods of length 5

In general, $A = 2[L(N + 1) + 1(N)] + 2(N - 1)$ for any length rod.

Another way to generalize the problem for any length L is to count the surfaces with an area of 1, or $2(2N - 1)$, and the surfaces with an area of L, or $2N + 2$. The total surface area is thus $A = 2(2N - 1)(1) + (2N + 2)(L)$.

6a. The dimensions are N, N, and 4.

6b. Possible equations: $A = 2(4N + N^2 + 4N)$, or $A = 2N^2 + 4(4N)$, or $A = 2N^2 + 16N$, or $A = 2N(N + 8)$

6c. $A = 2(10^2) + 16(10) = 360$ square units

6d. The relationship is quadratic. In the equation, the highest power of the variable is 2. The graph of the equation is a parabola.

Mathematical Reflections

In this investigation, you wrote equations to represent the surface area of a stack of rods. You saw that different ways of thinking about the surface area led to different equations. These questions will help you summarize what you have learned:

1 a. Describe at least two of the strategies your class used to find the surface area of the stacks.

b. Choose two of the strategies you described in part a, and show how they can be represented symbolically.

2 a. Describe situations that can be represented by several different, but equivalent, expressions. Explain how each expression represents a different way of thinking about the situation.

b. For each situation you described in part a, use the distributive and commutative properties to show that the expressions are equivalent.

Think about your answers to these questions, discuss your ideas with other students and your teacher, and then write a summary of your findings in your journal.

Tips for the Linguistically Diverse Classroom

Original Rebus The Original Rebus technique is described in detail in *Getting to Know Connected Mathematics*. Students make a copy of the text before it is discussed. During the discussion, they generate their own rebuses for words they do not understand; the words are made comprehensible through pictures, objects, or demonstrations. Example: Question 2b—Key words for which students might make rebuses are *distributive* [$a(b + c) = ab + ac$], *commutative* ($2 + 3 = 3 + 2$), *equivalent* (=).

TEACHING THE INVESTIGATION

5.1 • Stacking Rods

In Investigation 1, students began to explore the idea of equivalence in the context of a geometric problem, a border of tiles around a pool. After developing an understanding of some of the properties of real numbers and methods of solving equations, they are in a much stronger position to analyze a more complex geometric problem and make sense of different solutions. In this problem, they have an opportunity to model a real situation with symbols, to find and compare equivalent expressions, to generalize from one situation to another, and to find a solution for a specific case by applying all their knowledge of symbolic equivalences and number properties.

Launch

Introduce students to this activity's manipulatives, Cuisenaire rods. Allow students to inspect the rods and to build staggered stacks of rods as pictured in the student edition. Make sure they know that the rods are available in lengths from 1 unit to 10 units. The lengths are as follows:

Color	Length
natural	1
red	2
light green	3
purple	4
yellow	5
dark green	6
black	7
brown	8
blue	9
orange	10

Hold up a unit rod (the natural color).

> This rod has a length of 1 unit.

Hold up one of the colored rods.

> How long is this rod?

By laying the unit rods next to the colored rod, students can measure the length of the colored rod. If you have an overhead set of Cuisenaire rods, demonstrate this at the projector.

Pose the question of how the surface area of the arrangement that is pictured—three rods of a specific color—can be found. Let students offer various ways to reason about this.

> In this problem, you will search for a strategy for finding the surface area of a staggered stack of rods for a given length rod. Later you will have a chance to test your strategy for rods of other lengths.

Have students work in pairs on the problem and the follow-up.

Explore

Distribute four to six rods of the same length and several unit rods to each pair of students. (If you don't have enough unit rods to go around, students can measure with centimeter rulers.) Give the same length rod to several pairs so that students can compare their findings in the follow-up. For example, you might have four pairs of students work with rods of length 4, four pairs work with rods of length 5, four pairs work with rods of length 6, and the remaining pairs work with rods of length 7.

Also distribute a large sheet of paper to each pair of students for making tables and drawing sketches to explain their strategies. They should clearly note on their display the length of the rod with which they are working.

Students will find various ways to approach the problem of writing an equation for the relationship between the surface area and the number of rods. Some will make a table and write an equation by analyzing the pattern in the data. Some will analyze the stack of rods from a geometric perspective and construct the equation from there.

If students are having trouble writing an equation, help them by asking them to explain how they calculated the surface area for each given number of rods. Look for clues in their explanations that will allow you to ask questions leading them to a way of capturing their ideas symbolically. For example, some students may count all the square faces (those with an area of 1 square unit) and all the rectangular (nonsquare) faces, compute the two areas, and add the totals. You could help them write "surface area of square faces" + "surface area of rectangular faces." Then ask what general pattern they see for the faces of each length; students may express the pattern in many ways.

You might also suggest that students use a table to help them focus on the patterns. Some may then see that the relationship is linear and write an equation from there.

The tables below are given for your convenience in helping students who are having trouble determining the surface area for staggered stacks of rods of a particular length.

Length 2

Number of rods	Surface area
1	10
2	18
3	26
4	34
5	42

Length 3

Number of rods	Surface area
1	14
2	24
3	34
4	44
5	54

Length 4

Number of rods	Surface area
1	18
2	30
3	42
4	54
5	66

Length 5

Number of rods	Surface area
1	22
2	36
3	50
4	64
5	78

Length 6

Number of rods	Surface area
1	26
2	42
3	58
4	74
5	90

Length 7

Number of rods	Surface area
1	30
2	48
3	66
4	84
5	102

Length 8

Number of rods	Surface area
1	34
2	54
3	74
4	94
5	114

Length 9

Number of rods	Surface area
1	38
2	60
3	82
4	104
5	126

Length 10

Number of rods	Surface area
1	42
2	66
3	90
4	114
5	138

In the follow-up, students are asked to compare their expressions with those written by other students for the same length rod. To make this easier, you might designate areas of the classroom for students to post their work for each length rod.

Follow-up question 3 asks students whether their equation will work for rods of a different length. Have other rods available for students to inspect if they choose to, and encourage them to test their theories by using actual rods.

Summarize

Allow students to share their equations and solution strategies for each length rod. If you have a set of overhead Cuisenaire rods, students can demonstrate their reasoning at the projector.

This summarizing activity can be an opportunity for students to show what they have learned in many different ways: they can make a logical oral argument for how the symbolic model is derived; they can use tables, graphs, or symbolic expressions to check equivalence; they can solve or simplify equations. Everyone can participate at some level, from building models to checking answers to, optionally, searching for a general equation that fits *all* lengths of rods.

There is more than one way to think about the problem and to write an expression for each length rod. Several ways of reasoning about rods of length 4 are described here.

- Students may make a table and recognize the pattern as linear. Since an increase of 1 in the number of rods is related to an increase of 12 in the surface area, an equation is $A = 12N + 6$.

- Students may reason as follows: For one rod, the surface area is 18. For two rods, it is $18 + 12$. For three rods, it is $18 + 12 + 12$. For four rods, it is $18 + 12 + 12 + 12$. Thus, the surface area is always 18 plus $(N - 1)$ multiplied by 12, or $A = 18 + 12(N - 1)$.

Length 4

Number of rods	Surface area
1	18
2	30
3	42
4	54
5	66

- Students may analyze the number of surfaces with an area of 4 and the number of surfaces with an area of 1. The top and the front surfaces together have a surface area of $4(N + 1)$, and the right ends of the rods have a surface area of N. To account for the back, the bottom, and the left ends, double the areas, or $2[4(N + 1) + N]$. The number of additional surfaces with an area of 1, created by the staggering of the rods, is $2(N - 1)$. The total area is thus $2[4(N + 1) + N] + 2(N - 1)$.

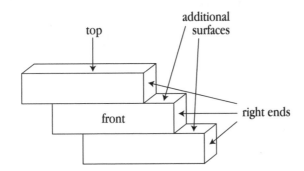

■ Students may analyze the number of surfaces with an area of 4 and the number of surfaces with an area of 1 in a different way. The number of surfaces with an area of 4 is $2N + 2$: N in the front, N in the back, and 1 on the top and the bottom. This is a total surface area of $4(2N + 2)$. The number of surfaces with an area of 1 is $2N + 2(N - 1)$: each rod has 2 ends, for $2N$ surfaces, plus the $N - 1$ surfaces uncovered by the staggering on each end of the stack, for $2(N - 1)$. This expression is multiplied by 1 to get the surface area. The total surface area is thus $4(2N + 2) + 2N + 2(N - 1)$.

■ Students might see a pattern in the number of surfaces with certain areas by making a table. Reasoning about the pattern leads to the equation $A = [2 + 4(N - 1)](1) + [4 + 2(N - 1)](4)$ or to the equation $A = (4N - 2)(1) + (2N + 2)(4)$.

Number of rods	Faces with an area of 1	Faces with an area of 4	Total surface area
1	2	4	$2(1) + 4(4) = 18$
2	6	6	$6(1) + 6(4) = 30$
3	10	8	$10(1) + 8(4) = 42$
4	14	10	$14(1) + 10(4) = 54$
$\vdots$			
N	$2 + 4(N - 1)$	$4 + 2(N - 1)$	$[2 + 4(N - 1)](1) + [4 + 2(N - 1)](4)$
or			
N	$4N - 2$	$2N + 2$	$(4N - 2)(1) + (2N + 2)(4)$

■ Some students may form the rods into a rectangular prism. For rods of length 4, this prism has dimensions N, 4, and 1. The surface area of the prism, $2(4N + N + 4)$, is then adjusted for the number of faces with a surface area of 1 that are hidden in the arrangement, a total of $2(N - 1)$.

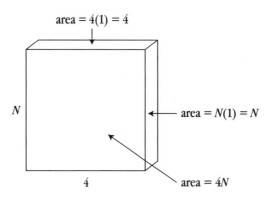

area = 4(1) = 4

N

4

area = $N(1) = N$

area = $4N$

The area of each face of the prism plus the lost area is $2(4N + N + 4) + 2(N - 1)$, or $2(5N + 4) + 2(N - 1)$.

- Some students may analyze the surface area of the figure as seen from the front, the right side, and the top; add the three numbers; and then multiply the sum by 2 to account for the back, the left side, and the bottom.

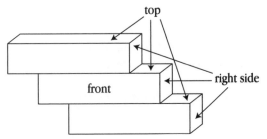

For rods of length 4, they might then produce the table below, which leads to the equation $A = 2[4N + N + 4 + (N - 1)]$, or to $A = 2(4N + N + N + 3)$, or $A = 2(6N + 3)$.

Number of rods	Surface area from front	Surface area from right side	Surface area from top	Total surface area
1	4	1	4	$2(4 + 1 + 4) = 18$
2	8	2	5	$2(8 + 2 + 5) = 30$
3	12	3	6	$2(12 + 3 + 6) = 42$
4	16	4	7	$2(16 + 4 + 7) = 54$
⋮				
N	$4N$	N	$4 + (N - 1)$	$2[4N + N + 4 + (N - 1)]$
or				
N	$4N$	N	$N + 3$	$2(4N + N + N + 3) = 2(6N + 3)$

Once all the expressions for a certain length rod have been offered, ask students to check that they are all equivalent by using what they have learned about number properties to transform one expression into another.

When there is agreement on the equations for each length rod, ask:

Can you see a pattern among these equations?

A list of all the equations students have written may help them discover a pattern, particularly if the equations are written in a particular form. As a class, identify the equation written in the form $y = mx + b$ for each length rod, or apply the distributive and commutative properties until each equation is in this form. The equations for all the rod lengths are given below.

Length (cm)	Equation in the form $y = mx + b$
2	$A = 8N + 2$
3	$A = 10N + 4$
4	$A = 12N + 6$
5	$A = 14N + 8$
6	$A = 16N + 10$
7	$A = 18N + 12$
8	$A = 20N + 14$
9	$A = 22N + 16$
10	$A = 24N + 18$

Once several of the equations are on the board, students should see a pattern.

> What kind of relationship do these equations represent? *(linear relationships)*

> What does the slope in each equation represent? *(the increase in the surface area created by the addition of another rod to the stack)*

> What does the *y*-intercept represent? *(the surface area for a stack of no rods)*

Obviously, a non-existent stack would have no surface area, so the *y*-intercept has no physical meaning. However, the equation does accurately represent the data for integer values of N equal to or greater than 1.

> Can you write an equation for the *volume* of a stack of N rods of length 4? *(Each rod has a volume of 4 cubic units, so the volume is 4N.)*

Encourage students who would enjoy a challenge to go beyond finding equations for each rod length to write an equation that gives the surface area of a staggered stack of rods for *any* length rod. In this case, there will be two variables—the number of rods, N, and the length of the rod, L. This exploration, which is presented as ACE question 5, also makes a good whole-class activity.

Additional Answers

Answers to Problem 5.1 Follow-Up

All answers given are for rods of length 4.

1. a. Using the distributive and commutative properties, students can show that the various expressions are equivalent. For example:

    $18 + 12(N - 1) = 18 + 12N - 12 = 12N + 6$

    $2[4(N + 1) + N] + 2(N - 1) = 2(4N + 4 + N) + 2N - 2 = 10N + 8 + 2N - 2 = 12N + 6$

    $4(2N + 2) + 2N + 2(N - 1) = 8N + 8 + 2N + 2N - 2 = 12N + 6$

    $(4N - 2)(1) + (2N + 2)(4) = 4N - 2 + 8N + 8 = 12N + 6$

    $2(4N + 4 + N) + 2N - 2 = 10N + 8 + 2N - 2 = 12N + 6$

    $2[4N + N + 4 + (N - 1)] = 2(6N + 3) = 12N + 6$

b. Equations that seem to have the same tables and graphs are likely to be equivalent, so you could make tables or graphs for all the expressions and compare them. (Note: Although the number of rods must be an integer equal to or greater than 1, the graph helps show the trend in the data.)

Length 4

Number of rods	Surface area
1	18
2	30
3	42
4	54
5	66
6	78

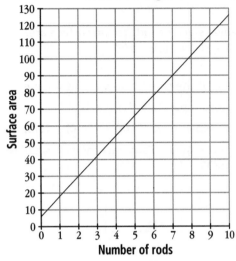

Rods of Length 4

ACE Answers

Applications

2c. $258 = 18 + 12(N - 1)$

$258 = 18 + 12N - 12$

$258 = 6 + 12N$

$252 = 12N$

$21 = N$ The number of rods must be 21.

Check:

$A = 18 + 12(N - 1)$

$258 = 18 + 12(21 - 1)$

$258 = 18 + 12(20)$

$258 = 18 + 240$

$258 = 258$

$A = 4(2N + 2) + 2(2N - 1)(1)$

$258 = 4(42 + 2) + 2(41)(1)$

$258 = 4(44) + 82$

$258 = 176 + 82$

$258 = 258$

Mathematical Reflections

1a. To find the surface area, you can find the area of each face and then find the sum of the areas. This can be simplified by noticing that some of the faces are identical. Also, you can make a table of data and look for a pattern in the table.

1b. Looking at the patterns in the stack of rods of length 4 might yield the equations $A = 4N + 4N + N + N + (N + 3) + (N + 3)$, or $A = 2[4(N + 1) + N] + 2(N - 1)$, or $A = 2[4(N) + 1(N) + 4(1)] + 2(N - 1)$. Looking at patterns in the table might yield the equations $A = 18 + 12(N - 1)$ or $A = 12N + 6$.

2a. *Situation 1:* Three ways to find the surface area of a staggered stack of 4 rods of length 3 are as follows:

■ Add the areas as viewed from the front, the top, and the left side, and multiply by 2 to account for the back, the bottom, and the right side: 2[4(3) + 6(1) + 4(1)]

■ Add the areas of the surfaces with an area of 3 to the areas of the surfaces with an area of 1: 3(10) + 1(14)

■ Add the surface area of a 3-by-4-by-1 stack of rods to the surface area of the "stairs" created by staggering the rods: 2[3(4) + 3(1) + 1(4)] + 1(6)

Situation 2: Three ways to find the area of the room below are as follows:

■ Calculate the top and bottom sections separately: 5(10) + 10(30)

■ Calculate the three vertical sections separately: 10(15) + 15(10) + 10(5)

■ Surround the layout with a large rectangle and subtract the two small rectangular areas that are not part of the room: 15(30) – 5(15) – 5(5)

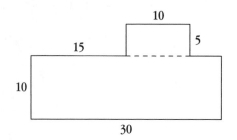 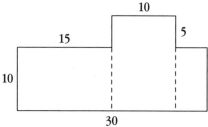 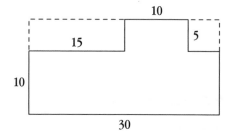

2b. *Situation 1:*
2[4(3) + 6(1) + 4(1)] = 2(12 + 6 + 4) = 2(22) = 44
3(10) + 1(14) = 30 + 14 = 44
2[3(4) + 3(1) + 1(4)] + 1(6) = 2(12 + 3 + 4) + 6 = 2(19) + 6 = 38 + 6 = 44

Situation 2:
5(10) + 10(30) = 50 + 300 = 350
10(15) + 15(10) + 10(5) = 150 + 150 + 50 = 350
15(30) – 5(15) – 5(5) = 450 – 75 – 25 = 350

Counting Cubes

Study the sequence of cube buildings below. What pattern do you see? Use the pattern to build the next building in the sequence. Think about the steps you are taking as you construct your building. The labels below the drawing illustrate one way you might think about the pattern.

  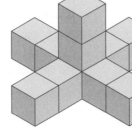

1 cube   1 cube in the center and   1 cube in the center and
                5 arms with 1 cube each   5 arms with 2 cubes each

1. Describe a pattern *you* see in the cube buildings.

2. Use your pattern to write an expression for the number of cubes in the nth building. You may find it helpful to make a table to organize your thinking.

3. Use your expression to find the number of cubes in the fifth building. Check your result by constructing the fifth building and counting the cubes.

4. Look for a different pattern in the buildings. Describe the pattern, and use it to write a different expression for the number of cubes in the nth building.

Assigning the Unit Project

The unit project can be used as the final assessment of this unit. It allows students to apply what they have learned about writing algebraic expressions to describe patterns that they observe and about verifying the equivalence of expressions written to describe the same pattern.

Students first explore the pattern in the cube buildings that are pictured in the student edition, writing various expressions to describe the pattern and checking the equivalence of those expressions. They then create their own sequences of cube buildings to investigate.

Students will need a set of cubes for this project. Ideally, each student will have at least 60 cubes; sugar cubes will work fine. Students may want to use isometric dot paper as well.

A guide to the project can be found in the Assessment Resources section.

5. Start with one of the expressions you wrote, and use the distributive and commutative properties to write a third expression. Does the third expression suggest another pattern in the cube buildings? Explain.

6. Now make your own sequence of cube buildings by following a particular pattern.

   a. Sketch the first few buildings in your sequence, and write an expression for the number of cubes in the nth building.

   b. Challenge a classmate to describe the pattern in your buildings and to use the pattern to write an expression for the number of cubes in the nth building.

   c. Compare the expression you wrote in part a to the expression written by your classmate. If the expressions are not identical, use the commutative and distributive properties to prove or disprove their equivalence.

Looking Back and Looking Ahead

Unit Reflections

Working on the problems of this unit you learned and practiced the standard rules for using symbolic expressions in algebra. You learned the *order of operations* rules for evaluating expressions when you were given values of the variables involved. You found properties of numbers and operations that can be used to write algebraic expressions in *equivalent forms* and to *solve linear* and *quadratic equations* with algebraic reasoning.

Using Your Algebraic Reasoning—To test your understanding and skill in use of algebraic notation and reasoning, consider several problems that arise in the business of managing a summer concert tour for a popular music group.

1 *The promoter pays appearance fees to each group on the concert program. Some groups also get a share of the ticket sale income. Suppose that*

- *the lead group will be paid $15,000, plus $5 for every ticket sold.*
- *one of the other groups will receive $1500, plus $1.50 for every ticket sold.*
- *the third group will receive a flat fee of $1250.*

a. Write three different but equivalent equations showing how the promoter's expenses for performers, E, depend on the number of tickets sold for the concert, t.

i. Write the first equation to show payments to each separate group.

ii. Write the second equation to show the payment to the lead group and the combined payments to the other groups.

iii. Write the third equation to show the simplest calculation of the total amount paid to the performers.

b. Suppose that tickets are priced at $25, $30, and $40.

i. Write an equation that shows how the promoter's income from ticket sales, I, depends on the number sold of each type of ticket, x, y, and z.

ii. Find the average income per ticket if there are sales of 5000 tickets at $25, 3000 tickets at $30, and 950 tickets sold at $40.

Answers

Using Algebraic Reasoning

1a. i. $E = (5t + 15{,}000) + (1.5t + 1500) + 1250$

ii. $E = (5t + 15{,}000) + (1.5t + 2750)$

iii. $E = 6.5t + 17{,}750$

b. i. $I = 25x + 30y + 40z$

ii. $28.27

iii. See page 72b.

How to Use
Looking Back and Looking Ahead: Unit Reflections

The first part of this section includes problems that allow students to demonstrate their mathematical understandings and skills. The second part gives them an opportunity to explain their reasoning. This section can be used as a review to help students stand back and reflect on the "big" ideas and connections in the unit. This section may be assigned as homework, followed up with class discussion the next day. Focus on the *Explaining Your Reasoning* section in the discussion. Encourage the students to refer to the problems to illustrate their reasoning.

1b iii. $V = \dfrac{25x + 30y + 40z}{t}$

2a. 8000

b. $32.50

c. If the price = $0, the number "sold" will be 10,000. For each increase of $1 in price, the number sold decreases by 200.

d. $I = s \times p$

$I = 10{,}000p - 200p^2$

e. $50. (The "price" of $0 would also yield an "income" of $0.)

f. $25

---

iii. Write an equation showing how the average income per ticket sold, V, depends on the variables x, y, z, and t.

2 *Suppose that the lead group has a new CD that will be sold only at concerts during the tour. Experience from other concert tours tells that the relation between the number of CDs sold, s, and price in dollars for the CD, p, can be modeled by the equation* $s = 10{,}000 - 200p$.

a. If the price is $10, how many CDs will likely be sold?

b. What price(s) will yield sales of 3500 CDs?

c. What do the numbers 10,000 and -200 tell about the relation between CD price and the number that will be sold at a typical concert?

d. Write an equation expressing the income, I, from CD sales in terms of s and p. Then write another equation expressing I only in terms of p, the price of the CD.

e. What price(s) will yield total income of $0?

f. What price(s) will yield maximum income?

3 *Suppose that concert seating is usually arranged in three sections as shown. Specific dimensions of the sections vary depending on the space available at each concert site.*

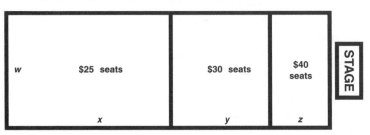

a. Write two equivalent equations showing the area of the entire seating area, A.

i. In one equation, show how A depends on the areas of the three seating sections.

ii. In the other equation, write an equivalent expression that requires fewer calculations to find A.

b. Seating is arranged to allow one square meter of space for every 2 people. Write two equivalent equations that show the number of seats, S, in terms of w, x, y, and z.

i. In one equation, show how S depends on the numbers of seats in the separate sections.

ii. In the other equation, write an expression that requires fewer calculations to find S.

74 Say It with Symbols

3a. i. $A = wx + wy + wz$

ii. $A = w(x + y + z)$

b. i. $S = 2wx + 2wy + 2wz$

ii. $S = 2w(x + y + z)$

c. $A = 4(1.5w) + 2(1.5x) + 2(1.5y) + 2(1.5z) + 8(1.5)^2 = 6w + 3x + 3y + 3z + 18$
Students who don't consider the 8 corner squares where the boards covering the aisles meet will omit $8(1.5)^2$ in computing the area.

c. When the concert is on a grassy field, aisles around and between the seating sections must be covered with boards that are 1.5 meters wide. How many square meters of board will be needed to cover the aisles for any given set of dimensions $w, x, y,$ and z? Express your answer in at least two equivalent ways.

Explaining Your Reasoning—When you solve problems by writing and operating on symbolic expressions, you have to be careful to follow standard rules for use of such expressions and operations. When you present your conclusions to others, you should be able to explain your reasoning by application of those rules.

1. Evaluate the following expressions for the given values of x and y. Be prepared to explain the reasons for your answers.

   a. $5(x + 12y)$ when $x = -7$ and $y = 0.5$

   b. $15 - 8x^2$ when $x = -3$

   c. $\frac{5x^2 - 4x}{7 - 3x}$ when $x = -2$

2. Write each of the following expressions in two different but equivalent forms. Be prepared to explain why the new forms are equivalent to those that are given.

   a. $7x(3 - 9x)$

   b. $15x + 8x^2$

   c. $(5x^2 - 9x + 7) + 4x(3 + 5x)$

   d. $(450 - 8a + 7b) - 3(5a - 2b)$

   e. $(2x + 3)(5x - 7)$

3. Solve the following equations by rewriting them in equivalent forms from which the roots are easy to find. Give the properties of numbers and operations that justify each step of your solution process.

   a. $9.5x + 12.5 = 50.5$ **b.** $3x^2 + 12x = 0$

   c. $(x + 4)(3x - 6) = 0$ **d.** $2(9x + 15) = 8 + 2x$

4. What does it mean to say that two algebraic expressions are *equivalent*?

The algebraic ideas and techniques you've used in this unit will be applied and extended in future mathematics courses and in science and business problems. The rules for expressing relationships among variables and for solving given equations are consistent around the world and in every discipline!

Explaining Your Reasoning

1a. Multiply 12 by 0.5, add –7, and multiply the sum by 5. The result is –5.

   b. Square –3, multiply that result by 8, and subtract the product from 15. The result is –57.

   c. For the numerator: Square –2, multiply that result by 5. The product is 20. Multiply –2 by 4, and then subtract that result, –8, from the earlier product of 20. The difference is 28.

For the denominator: Multiply –2 by 3 and subtract the result, –6, from 7. The difference is 13.

Divide the numerator by the denominator to get $\frac{28}{13}$ or about 2.15.

---

2. Some of the more obvious possibilities are included.

   a. $21x - 63x^2$ or $21x(1 - 3x)$

   b. $x(15 + 8x)$ or $8x^2 + 15x$

   c. $5x^2 - 9x + 7 + 12x + 20x^2$ or $25x^2 + 3x + 7$

   d. $450 - 8a + 7b - 15a + 6b$ or $-23a + 13b + 450$

   e. $10x^2 - 14x + 15x - 21$ or $10x^2 + x - 21$

3, 4. See page 72d.

Looking Back and Looking Ahead

Answers

3. Many solution paths are possible for each equation. One sample is shown for each.

    a. $9.5x = 38$ (subtract 12.5 from each side)

          $x = 4$ (divide each side by 9.5)

    b. $3x(x + 4) = 0$ (use the distributive property to factor the expression)

          $x = 0$ and $x = -4$ (use the zero product property)

    c. $x + 4 = 0$ when $x = -4$ and $3x - 6 = 0$ when $x = 2$, so the original equation has roots -4 and 2.

    d. $18x + 30 = 8 + 2x$ (use the distributive property)

          $16x = -22$ (subtract $2x$ and 30 from both sides)

            $x = -\frac{22}{16} = -1\frac{3}{8}$ or $x = -1.375$

4. Equivalent expressions give the same value for any given values of the variables involved.

Assessment Resources

For the quiz, students may need to be reminded of the formula for the circumference of a circle.

Check-Up 1

1. Alicia's summer job is to collect entry fees at a county park. Entry fees are $10 per day for buses and $1 per day for cars. At the end of each day, Alicia totals the entry fees and turns in an account sheet with the collected money. One day, 7 cars and 13 buses entered the park. Alicia entered $7 + 13 \times 10$ in her old calculator, in that order, and got 200 for an answer. This did not agree with the amount of the money Alicia had collected.

   a. In what order did the calculator perform the operations?

   b. To get the correct answer, in what order should Alicia perform the operations?

   c. What is the correct answer?

In 2–4, evaluate the expression for the given x value, and describe the order in which you performed the operations.

2. $^-5x + 9$ when $x = 3$

3. $3(x - 2) + 10$ when $x = ^-3$

4. $5x^2 - 2x + 6$ when $x = 4$

In 5–7, determine whether the expression has been evaluated correctly for $D = 33$. If an error has been made, explain the error and give the correct solution.

5. $\frac{175 + 33}{D} = \frac{175 + 33}{33} = 175 + 1 = 176$

6. $3.14 \times D^2 = 3.14 \times 1089 = 3419.46$

7. $\frac{33}{2D + 1} = \frac{1}{2 + 1} = \frac{1}{3}$

Quiz

In 1 and 2, insert parentheses to make the statement true.

1. $10 + 9x - 4x = 15x$

2. $10 + 9x - 4x = 5x + 2$

3. Jordan, the class treasurer, is responsible for keeping track of the expenses for the fall dance. While it is not important to make a profit, Jordan would like to at least break even. He made the following estimates of expenses and income. Notice that some of the expenses and income are fixed and some depend on the number of people who attend.

Expenses	**Income**
Sound equipment rental: $200	Ticket for 9th grade student: $3
Decorations: $50	Ticket for 8th grade student: $1.50
Refreshments: 50 cents per person	Donation from student council: $100

    a. Recall that profit = income – expenses. Suppose n ninth grade students and e eighth grade students attend the dance. Write two different expressions for profit. Explain why the two expressions are equivalent.

    b. Give an example of values of n and e that would create a profit.

Quiz

AutoParts, Inc., makes fan belts for all types of engines. The belts are made from lengths of rubber.

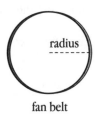

radius

fan belt

4. **a.** What length of rubber is needed to make a fan belt with a radius of 18 centimeters?

b. How much *more* rubber does it take to make a fan belt with a radius of 19 centimeters than one with a radius of 18 centimeters?

c. How much *more* rubber does it take to make a fan belt with a radius of 20 centimeters than one with a radius of 19 centimeters?

d. How much *more* rubber does it take to make a fan belt with a radius of 21 centimeters than one with a radius of 20 centimeters?

5. Robby is rebuilding the engine in his sports car. He needs to replace a fan belt with one that has a radius 1 centimeter greater than the radius of the original belt. AutoParts charges 10¢ per centimeter for all fan belts. AutoParts says that the larger size will cost Robby 63¢ more than the original size would cost. How could they have calculated the cost for the new belt without knowing the size of the original belt?

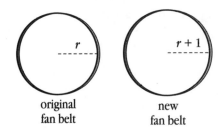

r

original
fan belt

$r + 1$

new
fan belt

Hint: Write an expression for the circumference of the *original* fan belt. Write a second expression for the circumference of the *new* fan belt. Both expressions should include the variable *r*, which represents the radius of the original belt. Compare your two expressions.

Name _____ Date _____

In 1 and 2, use the symbolic method to solve the equation. Show each step in your reasoning.

1. $7x - 10 = 10x - 15$ **2.** $4 + 3(x - 2) = x + 2$

3. a. The graph shown is of the equation $y = x^2 - 10x$.
    Explain how to use the graph to solve $x^2 - 10x = 0$.

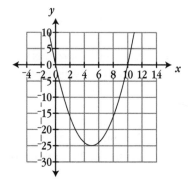

  b. Explain how to solve $x^2 - 10x = 0$ without using
    a table or a graph.

4. A travel agent made arrangements for the school basketball team and supporters to travel to the state tournament. The agent wrote the following equation for the profit she expected to make:

$$P = n(120 - n) - 50n, \text{ where } n \text{ is the number of students}$$

  a. Write two other equations for the profit by applying the distributive and commutative properties.

      $P =$ _____ $P =$ _____

  b. Use one of *your* equations to determine for what number of students the travel agent will break even. Explain your reasoning.

Assign these questions as additional homework, or use them as review, quiz, or test questions.

1. Which of the following expressions represent the *total* volume of the cylinder? There is more than one correct expression. You should be able to identify the correct choices without using your calculator. Explain why each expression you choose is correct.

$50(9 - 5)$ $50(5 + 4)$ $50 \times 5 + 50 \times 4$ $50 \times 5 \times 4$

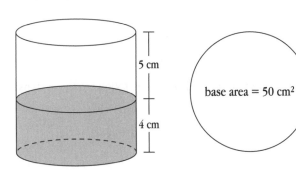

5 cm

4 cm

base area = 50 cm²

2. The large bike has a wheel with a radius that is 1 inch greater than that of the small bike's wheel.

small bike

large bike

a. Make a table like the one below to compare the distance traveled by the two bikes in one turn of the wheel. All measurements are in inches.

Radius of small bike wheel	Distance traveled by small bike in one turn of the wheel	Distance traveled by large bike in one turn of the wheel
10		
11		
12		
13		

b. Let r represent the radius of the small bike wheel. Write two equations, one for the distance, D_{small}, traveled by the small bike in one turn of the wheel and one for the distance, D_{large}, traveled by the large bike in one turn of the wheel.

$D_{small} =$ _____ $D_{large} =$ _____

c. Compare the two equations you wrote. How is the difference between your two equations reflected in the table?

3. Which of the following expressions represent the perimeter of the shape below? Explain why each expression you choose is correct.

$$2r + r + 2\pi r + r \qquad 4r + \pi r \qquad 2r + \pi r \qquad r(2 + \pi) \qquad r(4 + \pi)$$

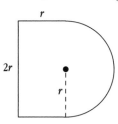

4. **a.** Write a formula for the area of the trapezoid shown by following these steps:

    Area of triangle 1 = _____

    Area of triangle 2 = _____

    Area of the trapezoid = _____

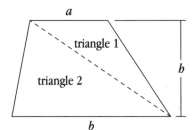

    b. The area of a trapezoid is often represented by the formula $\frac{1}{2}(a + b)h$. Explain or show how this formula is equivalent to your formula.

5. The manager of the Pine Cone restaurant wants to encourage more customers to come to his Monday night buffet. Right now *no one* comes when the price of the buffet is $15.00. He believes that if he lowers the price, more people will come. He estimates that he will attract 1 more customer for every $0.10 he drops the price.

    a. Make a table like the one below to calculate the income for certain numbers of customers.

Customers	Price per meal	Income
0	$15.00	
1	14.90	
2	14.80	
3		
4		

    b. Write an equation for the income, *I*, based on the number of customers, *n*. Sketch a graph of your equation.

    c. What equation could you solve to answer this question: "What number of customers will produce an income of $500?" Mark and label any points on the graph that represent the solution to your equation.

    d. What equation could you solve to answer this question: "What number of customers will produce an income of $0?" Mark and label any points on the graph that represent the solution to your equation.

    e. Make up another question about the situation, and explain how to answer it using the table or the graph.

6. **a.** Circle all solutions in the table to $100 + 2x < 140$.

x	y
16	132
17	134
18	136
19	138
20	140
21	142
22	144

  b. Use what you have learned about solving equations symbolically to determine values of x that satisfy the inequality $100 + 2x < 140$.

7. Solve the following equation, and check your answer.

$$^{-}3x + 3.5 = 3x - 3.1$$

8. Masako arranges hiking trips along the coast of California. Masako's friend Rod has written the equation $P = n(120 - n) - 50n$, where n is the number of people on a trip, to represent Masako's profit from a particular trip.

  a. Masako asks Rod a question about the situation, and he answers, "Between 30 and 40 people." What question did Masako ask? You may want to make a table to help you think about this.

  b. Write an equation or an inequality that models Masako's question.

  c. Sketch a graph of the profit equation on the axes below. Explain how you could use the graph to answer Masako's question.

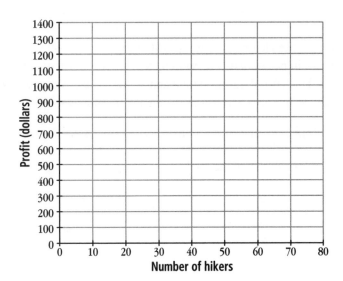

Name _____ Date _____

1. Kiran's family are remodeling their home. The wall between the living room and dining room will be removed to create one large room. Write two equivalent expressions for the area of the new room.

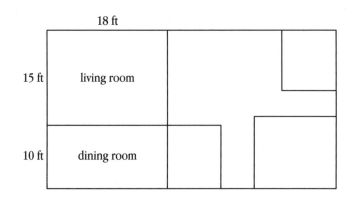

2. Three of the following expressions are equivalent. For the expression that is *not* equivalent to the others, explain how you can tell, without using your calculator, that it is not equivalent.

   $2x - 12x + 10$ $12x - 2x + 10$ $10 - 10x$ $10(1 - x)$

In 3 and 4, write an expression that is equivalent to the given expression.

3. $(15 - 4x) - (10 - x)$ 4. $3(10 + x) - (30 + 3x)$

5. Leon is in charge of the finances for a camping trip. There are 18 students from 12 different families going on the trip. Food will cost $7.50 per student and camping fees are $3.50 per student. In addition, each family will contribute $2 toward the cost of transportation and $1 toward the cost of a prize for the talent show to be held on the last night of the trip. Leon figures the total cost as follows:

   $$18 \times \$7.50 + 18 \times \$3.50 + 12 \times \$2 + 12 \times \$1 = \$234$$

   Write another expression for calculating the total.

6. Explain how can you tell, without using a calculator, that these expressions are *not* equivalent.

   $5 - 4x^2$ $\qquad\qquad$ $4x^2 - 5$ $\qquad\qquad$ $4x(x - 5)$

7. **a.** Circle all values in the table that represent solutions to $100 + 2x = 12x - 10$.

   b. Solve the equation $100 + 2x = 12x - 10$ symbolically, and check your answer.

x	$y = 100 + 2x$	$y = 12x - 10$
8	116	86
9	118	98
10	120	110
11	122	122
12	124	134
13	126	146
14	128	158

8. **a.** Circle all values in the table that represent solutions to $x^2 - 5x = 0$.

   b. Draw a double circle around all values in the table that represent solutions to $x^2 - 5x = 14$.

   c. Find the solution to $x^2 - 5x = 0$ by working with the equation.

x	$y = x^2 - 5x$
−2	14
−1	6
0	0
1	−4
2	−6
3	−6
4	−4
5	0
6	6
7	14
8	24

   d. Explain how a graph can be used to solve the equations $x^2 - 5x = 0$ and $x^2 - 5x = 14$.

Unit Test

In 9–11, determine whether the expression has been evaluated correctly for $D = 33$. If an error has been made, explain the error and give the correct answer.

9. $2023 - 23D = 2000 \times 33 = 66,000$

10. $20 + \frac{33}{D} = 20 + 1 = 21$

11. $\frac{1}{3} \times 3.14 \times D^2 = \frac{1}{3} \times 3.14 \times 33^2 = 3.14 \times 11^2 = 379.94$

12. Mr. Fern is in charge of the recycling program at Metropolis Middle School. He keeps track of the number of aluminum cans collected at school athletic events and the number of people who attend each event. Mr. Fern has found that, in general, the more people who attend an event, the more cans he can expect to collect. From his data, Mr. Fern developed the equation $C = 2.5(p - 40) - 100$, where C is the expected number of cans that will be collected and p is the number of people attending the event.

    a. If 100 people attend a basketball game, how many cans would Mr. Fern expect to collect?

    b. If 150 people attend a softball match, how many cans would Mr. Fern expect to collect?

    c. Batina works with Mr. Fern in the recycling program. She says that, based on her analysis of the data, the equation for predicting the number of cans collected should be $C = 2.5(p - 80)$. Are Mr. Fern's and Batina's expressions for the number of cans equivalent? Explain your answer.

Unit Test

13. Find four matches among the following choices. A match might be between equivalent versions of an equation, between an equation and a graph, or between an equation and a table. You should be able to make four groups of three.

<u>A</u> ____ ____   <u>B</u> ____ ____   <u>C</u> ____ ____   <u>F</u> ____ ____

   Match 1   Match 2   Match 3   Match 4

A $y = x(x + 3)$	**B** $y = 3x - x^2$	
C $y = x^2 - 4x$	**D** $y = x(3 - x)$	
E $y = 3x^2 - 12x$	**F** $y = 3x(x - 4)$	

G

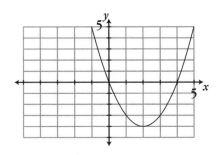

H

x	y
−2	36
−1	15
0	0
1	−9
2	−12
3	−9
4	0

I

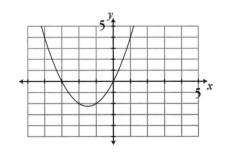

J

A parabola with a maximum point

K

x	y
−2	−2
−1	−2
0	0
1	4
2	10
3	18
4	28

L

x	y
−2	12
−1	5
0	0
1	−3
2	−4
3	−3
4	0

Notebook Checklist

Journal Organization

_____ Problems and Mathematical Reflections are labeled and dated.

_____ Work is neat and is easy to find and follow.

Vocabulary

_____ All words are listed.   _____ All words are defined or described.

Check-Ups and Quiz

_____ Check-Up 1   _____ Quiz

_____ Check-Up 2

Homework Assignments

____ _____

____ _____

____ _____

____ _____

____ _____

____ _____

____ _____

____ _____

____ _____

____ _____

____ _____

____ _____

____ _____

____ _____

____ _____

© Dale Seymour Publications®

Self-Assessment

Vocabulary

Of the vocabulary words I defined or described in my journal, the word _____ best demonstrates my ability to give a clear definition or description.

Of the vocabulary words I defined or described in my journal, the word _____ best demonstrates my ability to use an example to help explain or describe an idea.

Mathematical Ideas

1. **a.** In *Say It with Symbols,* I learned these things about . . .

    . . . evaluating numeric and symbolic expressions:

    . . . recognizing equivalent expressions and rewriting expressions:

    . . . solving linear equations:

    . . . solving quadratic equations:

    b. Here are page numbers of journal entries that give evidence of what I have learned, along with descriptions of what each entry shows:

2. **a.** These are the mathematical ideas I am still struggling with:

    b. This is why I think these ideas are difficult for me:

    c. Here are page numbers of journal entries that give evidence of what I am struggling with, along with descriptions of what each entry shows:

Class Participation

I contributed to the classroom discussion and understanding of *Say It with Symbols* when I . . . (Give examples.)

Answer Keys

Answers to Check-Up 1

1. **a.** The calculator added 7 and 13 and multiplied the sum by 10.

   b. Alicia should multiply the 13 and 10 and add 7 to the product.

   c. $137

2. $-5(3) + 9 = -15 + 9 = -6$; Multiplication is done before addition.

3. $3(-3 - 2) + 10 = 3(-5) + 10 = -15 + 10 = -5$; Subtraction in the parentheses is done first, then multiplication, and then addition.

4. $5(4^2) - 2(4) + 6 = 5(16) - 2(4) + 6 = 80 - 8 + 6 = 78$. Exponentiation is done first, then multiplication, and then addition.

5. The sum in the numerator should be evaluated *before* division by 33. The correct solution is $\frac{208}{33}$.

6. The expression has been evaluated correctly.

7. The operations in the denominator should be performed first, $2(33) + 1 = 66 + 1 = 67$. The correct solution is $\frac{33}{67}$.

Answers to the Quiz

1. $(10 + 9)x - 4x = 15x$

2. $10 + 9x - 4x = 5(x + 2)$

3. **a.** Possible answers:

   $(3n + 1.50e + 100) - [200 + 50 + 0.50(n + e)]$

   $(3n + 1.50e + 100) - (250 + 0.50n + 0.50e)$

   $3n - 0.50n + 1.50e - 0.50e + 100 - 250$

   $2.50n + e - 150$

   b. Answers will vary. The values of n and e must be great enough to offset the loss created by the difference between the $100 donation and the $250 in expenses, plus the refreshment expense. That is, the expression $250n + e - 150$ must be positive.

4. **a.** $36\pi \approx 113.1$ cm

   b. $38\pi - 36\pi = 2\pi \approx 6.3$ cm more

   c. $40\pi - 38\pi = 2\pi \approx 6.3$ cm more

   d. $42\pi - 40\pi = 2\pi \approx 6.3$ cm more

5. The original fan belt would require $2\pi r$ centimeters of rubber. The new fan belt will require $2\pi(r + 1)$, or $2\pi r + 2\pi$, centimeters of rubber. The new belt requires 2π, or approximately 6.3, more centimeters of rubber than the old belt. This amount of rubber would cost 63¢. No matter what the original radius, an increase of 1 centimeter will result in an increase of 2π centimeters in the perimeter and an increase in cost of 63¢.

Answers to Check-Up 2

1.
$$7x - 10 = 10x - 15$$
$$7x - 10 - 7x = 10x - 15 - 7x$$
$$^-10 = 3x - 15$$
$$^-10 + 15 = 3x - 15 + 15$$
$$5 = 3x$$
$$\frac{5}{3} = \frac{3x}{3}$$
$$\frac{5}{3} = x$$

2.
$$4 + 3(x - 2) = x + 2$$
$$4 + 3x - 6 = x + 2$$
$$3x - 2 = x + 2$$
$$3x - 2 - x = x + 2 - x$$
$$2x - 2 = 2$$
$$2x - 2 + 2 = 2 + 2$$
$$2x = 4$$
$$\frac{2x}{2} = \frac{4}{2}$$
$$x = 2$$

3. **a.** The solutions to the equation are the x values at the points where the y value is zero, or $x = 0$ and $x = 10$.

   b. For $x^2 - 10x$ to equal 0, one of the factors in the factored form $x(x - 10)$ must equal 0: $x = 0$ or $x - 10 = 0$. Thus, $x = 0$ or $x = 10$.

4. **a.** Possible answer: $P = 120n - n^2 - 50n$ and $P = 70n - n^2$

   b. The break-even point can be found by setting the profit equation equal to 0:
   $$70n - n^2 = 0$$
   $$n(70 - n) = 0$$
   $$n = 0 \text{ or } n = 70 \qquad \text{The agent will break even at 0 students or 70 students.}$$

Answers to the Question Bank

1. The expressions $50(5 + 4)$ and $50 \times 5 + 50 \times 4$ both represent the cylinder's volume. In each expression, the area of the base, 50, is multiplied by the height of the cylinder, which is broken into two parts, 5 and 4.

2. **a.**

Radius of small bike wheel	Distance traveled by small bike in one turn of the wheel	Distance traveled by large bike in one turn of the wheel
10	62.8	69.1
11	69.1	75.4
12	75.4	81.7
13	81.7	88.0

   b. $D_{small} = 2\pi r$ $D_{large} = 2\pi (r + 1)$

   c. The equation for D_{large} can be rewritten as $D_{large} = 2\pi r + 2\pi$, which includes a 2π term that is not in the equation $D_{small} = 2\pi r$. The values for D_{large} should be 2π, or about 6.3, greater than the corresponding values for D_{small}. The entries in the third column are about 6.3 inches greater than the corresponding entries in the second column.

3. The expressions $4r + \pi r$ and $r(4 + \pi)$ both represent the figure's perimeter. Possible explanation: The perimeter of a circle is $2\pi r$, so the perimeter of the semicircular part is πr. The three sides of the rectangle, $2r$, r, and r, form the rest of the perimeter. The total is thus $2r + r + r + \pi r$, or $4r + \pi r$, which is equivalent to $r(4 + \pi)$.

4. **a.** area of triangle 1 $= \frac{1}{2}ab$

    area of triangle 2 $= \frac{1}{2}bh$

    area of the trapezoid $= \frac{1}{2}ab + \frac{1}{2}bh$

   b. $\frac{1}{2}ab + \frac{1}{2}bh = \frac{1}{2}(ab + bh) = \frac{1}{2}(a + b)h$

5. **a.**

Customers	Price per meal	Income
0	$15.00	$0.00
1	14.90	14.90
2	14.80	29.60
3	14.70	44.10
4	14.60	58.40

   b. $I = n(15 - 0.1n)$

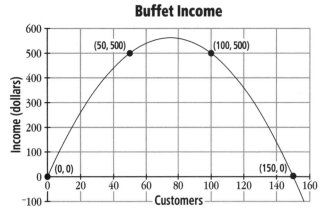

Buffet Income

   c. $500 = n(15 - 0.1n)$; The points $(50, 500)$ and $(100, 500)$ represent the answers to this question.

   d. $0 = n(15 - 0.1n)$; The points $(0, 0)$ and $(150, 0)$ represent the answers to this question.

   e. Possible questions: "How many customers will produce the greatest income?" (The answer, 75 customers, is found from the maximum point of the graph.) "How many customers will it take to produce an income of at least $400?" (The answer to this, between 35 and 115 customers, is found from the points in the graph where income is equal to $400.)

Answer Keys

6. **a.** Any value of x less than 20 is a solution to $100 + 2x < 140$.

x	y
⑯	132
⑰	134
⑱	136
⑲	138
20	140
21	142
22	144

b. Possible solution:
$$100 + 2x < 140$$
$$100 + 2x - 100 < 140 - 100$$
$$2x < 40$$
$$\frac{2x}{2} < \frac{40}{2}$$
$$x < 20$$

7. Possible solution:
$$-3x + 3.5 = 3x - 3.1$$
$$-3x + 3.5 + 3x = 3x - 3.1 + 3x$$
$$3.5 = 6x - 3.1$$
$$3.5 + 3.1 = 6x - 3.1 + 3.1$$
$$6.6 = 6x$$
$$\frac{6.6}{6} = \frac{6x}{6}$$
$$1.1 = x$$

Check:
$$-3(1.1) + 3.5 = 3(1.1) - 3.1$$
$$-3.3 + 3.5 = 3.3 - 3.1$$
$$0.2 = 0.2$$

8. **a.** The question was some form of "How many people must go on the hiking trip for my profit to be greater than $1200?" The answer can be seen in the table below. (Note: Students may also interpret Rod's answer as including 30 and 40.)

n	P
30	1200
㉛	1209
㉜	1216
㉝	1221
㉞	1224
㉟	1225
㊱	1224
㊲	1221
㊳	1216
㊴	1209
40	1200

b. $n(120 - n) - 50n > 1200$

Say It with Symbols | **Assessment Resources** 91

c.   Masako's profit will exceed $1200 at the points on the graph above $1200 on the profit axis, or for more than 30 people and fewer than 40 people.

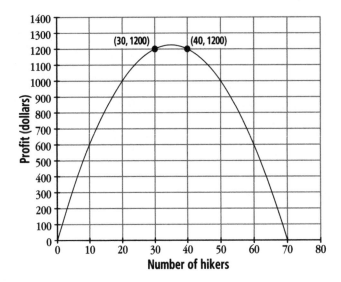

Answers to the Unit Test

1. $15(18) + 10(18)$ and $(15 + 10)18$

2.   The expression $12x - 2x + 10$ is not equivalent to the others; explanations will vary. The three other expressions are all equivalent to $10 - 10x$ while the expression $12x - 2x + 10$ is equivalent to $10 + 10x$.

3.   Possible answers: $15 - 4x - 10 + x$, $5 - 3x$

4.   Possible answers: $30 + 3x - 30 - 3x$, 0

5.   Possible answers: $18(\$7.50 + \$3.50) + 12(\$2 + \$1)$, $18(\$11) + 12(\$3)$

6.   Possible answer: The expressions $5 - 4x^2$ and $4x^2 - 5$ are not equivalent; the sign of each term in the first is opposite from that of the corresponding term in the second. The expressions $4x^2 - 5$ and $4x(x - 5)$ are not equivalent; if the third expression is expanded, it is $4x^2 - 20x$, which is different from $4x^2 - 5$. And $5 - 4x^2$ is not equivalent to $4x(x - 5)$, expanded to $4x^2 - 20x$, because the signs are different and the magnitudes of the coefficient of x are different.

7.   a.

x	$y = 100 + 2x$	$y = 12x - 10$
8	116	86
9	118	98
10	120	110
⑪	122	122
12	124	134
13	126	146
14	128	158

b. $100 + 2x = 12x - 10$ check: $100 + 2(11) = 12(11) - 10$
            $100 = 10x - 10$ $100 + 22 = 132 - 10$
            $110 = 10x$ $122 = 122$
              $11 = x$

8. a, b.

x	$y = x^2 - 5x$
-2	14
-1	6
0	0
1	-4
2	-6
3	-6
4	-4
5	0
6	6
7	14
8	24

(The values -2, 0, 5, and 7 are circled in the x column.)

c. $x^2 - 5x = 0$

$x(x - 5) = 0$

$x = 0$ or $x = 5$.

d. Graph the equation $y = x^2 - 5x$. The x-coordinates of the x-intercepts are the solutions to $x^2 - 5x = 0$. Use the calculator to find the points whose y-coordinates are 14. The x-coordinates of these points are the solutions to $x^2 - 5x = 14$. The intersection point of the graphs of $y = 14$ and $y = x^2 - 5x$ can also be used to find the solution to $x^2 - 5x = 14$.

9. The 23 should have been multiplied by 33 rather than subtracted from 2023. The correct answer is 1264.

10. The expression has been evaluated correctly.

11. The 33 should have been squared before being multiplied by $\frac{1}{3}$. The correct answer is 1139.82.

12. a. $2.5(100 - 40) - 100 = 50$ cans

b. $2.5(150 - 40) - 100 = 175$ cans

c. The expressions both simplify to $2.5p - 200$, so they are equivalent.

13. Match 1: A, I, K   Match 2: B, D, J   Match 3: C, G, L   Match 4: F, E, H

The assessment for *Say It with Symbols* includes two check-ups. Below is a suggested scoring rubric and a grading scale for Check-Up 1. Samples of two students' work and a teacher's comments about how the work was assessed follow.

Suggested Scoring Rubric

This rubric employs a scale with a total of 17 possible points. You may use the rubric as presented or modify it to fit your district's requirements for evaluating and reporting students' work and understanding.

question 1: 3 points
- 1 point for a correct and complete answer to each part

questions 2–4: 9 points (3 points each)
- 1 point for correctly evaluating the expression
- 1 point for giving a correct order of operations
- 1 point for using correct symbolic notation for the work shown (Note: This is included in the scoring because this is a primary focus of the unit.)

question 5: 2 points
- 1 point for noting that the solution is incorrect and identifying the error
- 1 point for finding the correct solution

question 6: 1 point
- 1 point for identifying that the solution is correct

question 7: 2 points
- 1 point for noting that the solution is incorrect and identifying the error
- 1 point for finding the correct solution

Grading Scale

Points	Grade
15 to 17	A
13 to 14	B
11 to 12	C
9 to 10	D

Sample 1

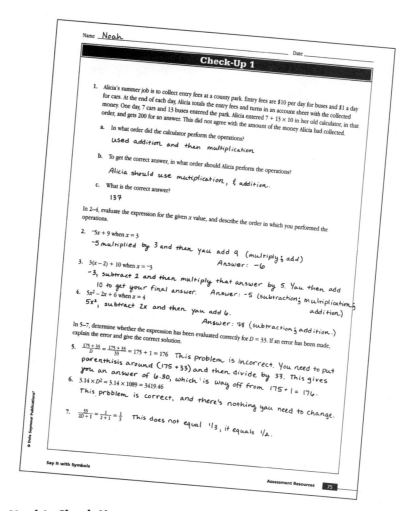

Name _Noah_   Date _____

Check-Up 1

1. Alicia's summer job is to collect entry fees at a county park. Entry fees are $10 per day for buses and $1 a day for cars. At the end of each day, Alicia totals the entry fees and turns in an account sheet with the collected money. One day, 7 cars and 13 buses entered the park. Alicia entered $7 + 13 \times 10$ in her old calculator, in that order, and gets 200 for an answer. This did not agree with the amount of the money Alicia had collected.

   a. In what order did the calculator perform the operations?
   used addition and then multiplication

   b. To get the correct answer, in what order should Alicia perform the operations?
   Alicia should use multiplication, & addition.

   c. What is the correct answer?
   _137_

In 2–4, evaluate the expression for the given x value, and describe the order in which you performed the operations.

2. $-5x + 9$ when $x = 3$
   -5 multiplied by 3 and then you add 9 (multiply; add)
                                    Answer: -6

3. $3(x - 2) + 10$ when $x = -3$
   -3, subtract 2 and then multiply that answer by 5. You then add 10 to get your final answer. Answer: -5 (subtraction; multiplication; addition)

4. $5x^2 - 2x + 6$ when $x = 4$
   5x², subtract 2x and then you add 6.
                        Answer: 78 (subtraction; addition.)

In 5–7, determine whether the expression has been evaluated correctly for $D = 33$. If an error has been made, explain the error and give the correct solution.

5. $\frac{175 + 33}{D} = \frac{175 + 33}{33} = 175 + 1 = 176$ _This problem is incorrect. You need to put parenthisis around (175 + 33) and then divide by 33. This gives you an answer of 6.30, which is way off from 175 + 1 = 176._

6. $3.14 \times D^2 = 3.14 \times 1089 = 3419.46$
   This problem is correct, and there's nothing you need to change.

7. $\frac{33}{2D + 1} = \frac{1}{2 + 1} = \frac{1}{3}$ _This does not equal ⅓, it equals ½._

Say It with Symbols

Assessment Resources   75

Teacher's Comments on Noah's Check-Up

Noah earned 12 of the 17 points. He correctly and completely addressed question 1 and received full credit.

Noah did not express all his work in questions 2–4 using symbols. Since the problems do not state that using symbolic notation is a requirement, I did not feel that I could deduct for Noah's choosing to answer the questions using a combination of symbols and words. He received full credit for question 2. For question 3, he received 2 of the 3 points because he gives an incorrect amount in his explanation; thus his work with symbols is incorrect. He writes "multiply that answer by 5" when he should have written "multiply that solution of -5 by 3." He received only 1 point for question 4 because, although he has the correct solution, his explanation of the order of operations is unclear and incomplete. He states that you take "$5x^2$, subtract $2x$." I am unsure what he means; are you to subtract first and then multiply, or do the exponentiation first, multiply, and then subtract?

Noah received full credit for question 5 although his explanation is not entirely clear. He received full credit for question 6 but no credit for question 7 as he did not correctly identify the error or give the correct solution.

Sample 2

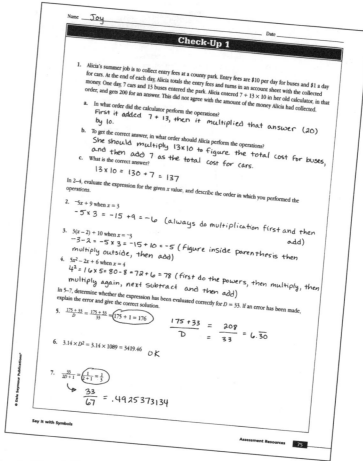

Teacher's Comments on Joy's Check-Up

Joy earned 15.5 points. For question 1, she received full credit; her answers were correct and complete.

For questions 2–4, Joy evaluated the expressions correctly and adequately explained the order of operations she used. However, in all three questions her notation was incorrect. For example, in her answer to question 2 she writes $-5 \times 3 = -15 + 10$. This notation matches the order in which she says she solved the problem, but the equality is mathematically incorrect. Because this is a unit on symbolic notation, her work leaves me with some concern about what sense she is making of symbols and their relationships. Yet, because she repeats this mistake in all three questions and the symbols she gives have some reasonable connection to the problem, I deducted only half a point for each question.

Joy answered questions 5–7 correctly and received full credit.

In summary, both students seem to have an understanding of order of operations. Yet, these two and many other students in my class seem to be struggling with the proper use of symbols. I need to spend more time discussing correct notation so that their symbols correctly represent their thinking and the relationships among expressions.

Guide to the Unit Project

The unit project can be used as the final assessment in *Say It with Symbols*. The project allows students to apply what they have learned about writing algebraic expressions to describe patterns that they observe and about verifying the equivalence of those expressions.

Students will need a set of cubes for this project. Ideally, each student will have at least 60 cubes, though students can work in small groups on parts 1 through 5. Sugar cubes will work fine, especially if students work at home on the project. Students may also want to use isometric dot paper for making their own sequences of cube buildings in part 6.

You may want to have students begin the project in class, sharing the patterns that they see in the sequence of cube buildings. This will help everyone realize that there are different ways to talk about and describe the pattern.

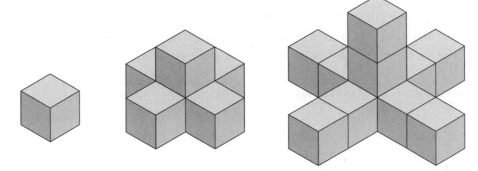

For part 6, each student is to make a new sequence of cube buildings, write an expression to represent the pattern in the buildings, and then have a classmate write an expression to represent it. Students are to compare the different expressions written for their sequences of cube buildings and use the algebraic properties they have learned to check their equivalence.

Possible Answers

1. Answers will vary. Some possibilities follow.
   - The buildings are composed of a central cube and 5 arms that contain 0 cubes, then 1 cube, then 2 cubes, then 3 cubes, and so on. (This pattern is described in the student edition.)
   - The buildings are composed of a central tower that contains 1 cube, then 2 cubes, then 3 cubes, and so on; and 4 arms that contain 0 cubes, then 1 cube, then 2 cubes, and so on.
   - Each new building is the previous building with 5 cubes added.
2. Students may have constructed tables to show the patterns. On the next page, an expression for the number of cubes in the nth building is given for each pattern described above.

- The buildings are composed of a central cube and 5 arms that contain 0 cubes, then 1 cube, then 2 cubes, then 3 cubes, and so on. An expression for the number of cubes in the nth building is $1 + 5(n - 1)$.

Building number, n	Cubes in center	Cubes in each of 5 arms
1	1	0
2	1	1
3	1	2
4	1	3
$\vdots$		
n	1	$n - 1$

- The buildings are composed of a central tower that contains 1 cube, then 2 cubes, then 3 cubes, and so on; and 4 arms that contain 0 cubes, then 1 cube, then 2 cubes, and so on. An expression for the number of cubes in the nth building is $n + 4(n - 1)$.

Building number, n	Cubes in tower	Cubes in each of 4 arms
1	1	0
2	2	1
3	3	2
4	4	3
$\vdots$		
n	n	$n - 1$

- Each new building is the previous building with 5 cubes added. This is a linear pattern in the form $y = mx + b$, where $m = 5$ and $b = {}^-4$, so an expression for the number of cubes in the nth building is $5n - 4$.

Building number, n	Total number of cubes
1	1
2	6
3	11
4	16
$\vdots$	
n	$5n - 4$

3. The fifth building contains 21 cubes, which can be determined by substituting into any correct expression: $1 + 5(n - 1) = 1 + 5(4) = 21$, $n + 4(n - 1) = 5 + 4(4) = 21$, and $5n - 4 = 5(5) - 4 = 21$.

4. See the answer to question 2.

5. Answers will vary. Students may find one of the patterns described above, or they may uncover a new pattern. Two examples are given here.

   - The expression $n + 4(n - 1)$ can be rewritten as $n + 4n - 4$, which could be interpreted as describing this pattern: Each building contains a tower of height n and 4 arms of length n. However, this counts the central cube 5 times, so we must subtract 4 to arrive at a correct expression.

   - The expression $1 + 5(n - 1)$ can be rewritten as $1 + 5n - 5$, which could be interpreted as describing this pattern: Each building contains one central cube and 5 arms of length n. However, this counts the central cube 6 times, so we must subtract 5 to arrive at a correct expression.

6. Answers will vary. Talk with students individually about the expressions written for their sequence of cube buildings to assess their understanding of using symbols to model a pattern and checking expressions for equivalence.

Blackline
Masters

Problem 3.3 Trapezoids

The marketing manager wants to make a table showing admission prices for groups with certain numbers of adults and children.

Group Admission Prices

		Number of children				
		20	40	60	80	100
Number of adults	10					
	20					
	30					
	40					

A. Copy and complete the table. Do your calculations without using a calculator.

B. Look for patterns in the rows and columns. Describe each pattern you find, and tell which part of the equation creates the pattern.

C. In the equation $p = 100 + 10a + 8c$, what do the numbers 100, 10, and 8 tell you about calculating the group price?

D. What mathematical operations do you need to perform to calculate the group price for a particular number of adults and children? In what order must you perform the operations?

The daily concession profit can be predicted by the equation $P = 2.50V - 500$. This profit equation was used to derive the following equation for the *average* daily concession profit per visitor:

$$A = \frac{2.50V - 500}{V}$$

A. **1.** If 300 people visit the park, about how much concession profit will be made?

   2. About how much concession profit will be made per visitor?

B. Copy and complete the table below to show the average per-visitor concession profit for various numbers of visitors. Do your calculations without using a calculator.

Visitors	100	200	300	400	500	600	700	800
Average profit								

C. Find the average per-visitor concession profit for 250, 350, and 425 visitors.

D. What mathematical operations do you need to perform to calculate the average per-visitor profit for a given number of visitors?

In what order must you perform the operations?

E. The Water Works business manager claims that the average concession profit per visitor can also be calculated with either of these equations:

$$A = \frac{1}{V}(2.50V - 500)$$

$$A = (2.50V - 500) \div V$$

Do you agree? Explain.

The equation below gives the height, y, of the arch above a point x feet from one of the bases of the arch. If you are standing under the arch x feet from one base, the point of the arch directly over your head will be $25x - 0.5x^2$ feet above the ground.

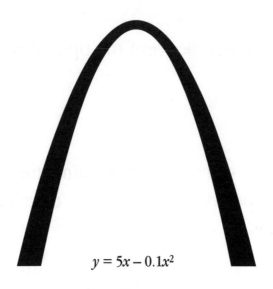

$$y = 5x - 0.1x^2$$

A. Use the equation to find the height of the arch at these distances from the left base. Do your calculations without using a calculator.

1. 10 feet

2. 30 feet

3. 50 feet

B. What operations did you perform to calculate your answers for part A? In what order did you perform these operations?

C. Check your answers for part A by using a graphing calculator to help you make a table.

D. 1. The expression $5x - 0.1x^2$ is equivalent to the expression $0.1x(50 - x)$. Use this second expression to calculate the heights for the x values given in part A.

2. In what order did you perform the operations?

If a square pool has sides of length *s* feet, how many tiles are needed to form the border?

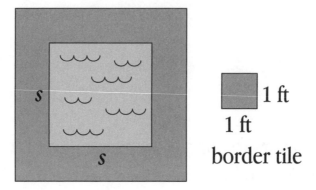

1 ft
1 ft
border tile

A. Make sketches on grid paper to help you figure out how many tiles are needed for borders of square pools with sides of length 1, 2, 3, 4, 6, and 10 feet. Record your results in a table.

B. Write an equation for the number of tiles, *N*, needed to form a border for a square pool with sides of length *s* feet.

C. Try to write at least one more equation for the number of tiles needed for the border of the pool. How could you convince someone that your expressions are equivalent?

Takashi thought of the pool's border as being composed of four 1-by-*s* rectangles, each made from *s* tiles, and four corner squares, each made from one tile. He wrote the expression 4*s* + 4 to represent the total number of border tiles.

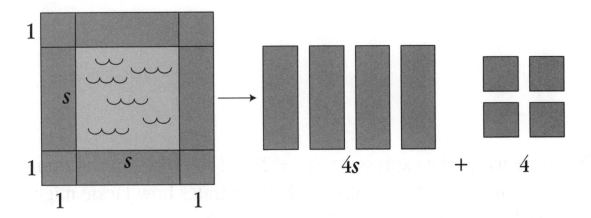

A. Stella wrote the expression 4(*s* + 1) to represent the number of border tiles. Draw a picture that illustrates how Stella might have been thinking about the border of the pool.

B. Jeri wrote the expression *s* + *s* + *s* + *s* + 4 to represent the number of border tiles. Draw a picture that illustrates how Jeri might have been thinking about the border of the pool.

C. Sal wrote the expression $2s + 2(s + 2)$ to represent the number of border tiles. Draw a picture that illustrates how Sal might have been thinking about the border of the pool.

D. Jackie wrote the expression $4(s + 2) - 4$ to represent the number of border tiles. Draw a picture that illustrates how Jackie might have been thinking about the border of the pool.

E. Explain why each expression in parts A–D is equivalent to Takashi's expression.

Below are four designs for pools with swimming and diving sections. For each design, show two methods for calculating the total surface area of the water. Then tell which method is more efficient. That is, tell which method requires fewer mathematical operations.

A.

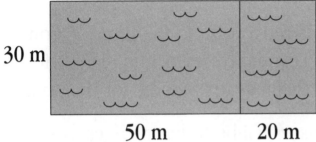

30 m

50 m   20 m

B.

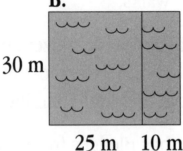

30 m

25 m   10 m

C.

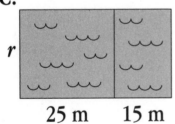

r

25 m   15 m

D.

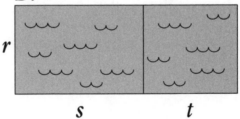

r

s   t

Leanne, Gilberto, and Alana are participating in a walkathon.

- Leanne asks her sponsors to pledge $1 for each mile she walks.
- Gilberto asks his sponsors to pledge $2 for each mile he walks.
- Alana asks her sponsors to pledge $5 plus $0.50 for each mile she walks.

The walkathon organizers have offered a prize to the three-person team that raises the most money. Leanne, Gilberto, and Alana will walk together and combine their earnings to compete for the prize.

Leanne has pledges from 16 sponsors, Gilberto has pledges from 7 sponsors, and Alana has pledges from 11 sponsors.

A. For each student, write an equation for the amount of money the student will raise if he or she walks x miles. Then write an equation for the total amount the three-person team will raise if they walk x miles.

$A_{Leanne} =$

$A_{Gilberto} =$

$A_{Alana} =$

$A_{total} =$

B. Alana asked each of her 11 sponsors to pledge $5 in addition to an amount per mile, so the team will raise $55 regardless of how far they walk.

    1. Excluding the $55, how much will the team raise per mile?

    2. Use your answer from part 1 to help you write a different equation for the total amount the team will raise if they walk x miles.

C. 1. Use the distributive and commutative properties to show that the two expressions you wrote for the total amount the team will raise are equivalent.

    2. Verify that the expressions are equivalent by making and comparing tables or graphs.

At their planning meeting, the organizers of the hospital walkathon discussed expenses and income. They made the following estimates:

- Expense for posters and newspaper, radio, and TV ads: $500

- Expense for souvenir T-shirts for participants: $6 per child, $8.50 per adult

- Income from business sponsors whose logos will appear on T-shirts and signs: $1000

- Expense for paramedics and an ambulance in case of emergency: $250

- Income from registration fees: $5 per child, $15 per adult

Notice that some of the expenses are fixed, while others depend on the number of adults and children who participate.

The difference between the total income and the total expenses is the profit. The organizers will donate any profit from the event to the hospital.

A. Estimate the total income, the total expenses, and the total profit if 40 children and 30 adults participate in the walkathon.

B. Write two equivalent expressions for the total income in terms of the number of adults, *a,* and the number of children, *c,* who participate.

C. Write two equivalent expressions for the total expenses in terms of the number of adults, *a,* and the number of children, *c,* who participate.

D. Use parentheses and your results from parts B and C to write an expression showing the profit as total income minus total expenses. That is, express the profit as (expression for income) − (expression for expenses).

E. Write an expression for profit that is equivalent to your expression from part D but that is as short as possible. Use the distributive and commutative properties to show that the two profit expressions are equivalent.

F. Evaluate your profit expressions from parts D and E for $a = 100$ and $c = 75$. Can you conclude from your results that the expressions are equivalent? Explain.

G. Compare the profit expressions you wrote in parts D and E. What are the advantages and disadvantages of writing the profit expression in a shorter form?

Tua, Sam, and Carlos made the drawings below to illustrate their methods for calculating the area of a trapezoid. Try to figure out how each student thought about the problem.

Tua's method

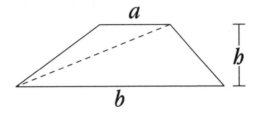

Sam's method

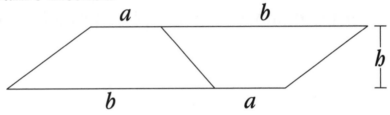

Carlos's method

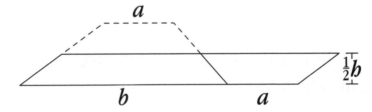

A. Explain each student's method for finding the area.

B. Write an algebraic expression to describe each method.

C. Show that the expressions you wrote in part B are equivalent.

In parts A–C, you will explore three ways of thinking about this question: If a league has n teams and each team plays each of the other teams twice, how many games are played in all?

A. Figure out how many games would be played for leagues with 2, 3, 4, 5, and 6 teams. Record your results in a table.

Number of teams	2	3	4	5	6
Number of games					

Look for a pattern in your table. Use the pattern to write an expression for the number of games played by a league with n teams.

B. Suppose a sports reporter wants to attend exactly one game in the schedule of an n-team league.

1. How many choices does the reporter have for the home team for the game she attends?

2. Once she has chosen a home team, how many choices does she have for the visiting team?

3. Use your answers from parts 1 and 2 to write an expression for the total number of games the reporter can choose from.

C. Suppose you made a table to record wins and losses for an
   n-team league.

Visiting Team

	T_1	T_2	T_3	$\cdots$	T_n
T_1					
T_2					
T_3					
$\vdots$					
T_n					

Home Team

1. How many cells would your table have?

2. How many cells in the table would not be used for *W* or
   L entries?

3. Use your answers from parts 1 and 2 to write an expression
   for the total number of games played.

D. In parts A–C, you wrote expressions for the number of games
   played by an *n*-team league. Show that these expressions are
   equivalent.

bid 1: cost = \$100 + \$4 × the number of books printed
bid 2: cost = \$25 + \$7 × the number of books printed

If you let x represent the number of books printed and y represent the cost in dollars, the equations become $y = 100 + 4x$ and $y = 25 + 7x$.

Use your graphing calculator to help answer parts A–C.

A. Make a table of x and y values for each bid. Use your table to find the number of books for which the two bids are equal. Explain your work.

B. Make a graph of the two equations. Use your graph to find the number of books for which the two bids are equal. Copy the graph onto your paper, and use it to help explain how you found your answer.

C. For what numbers of books is bid 1 less than bid 2? Explain how you found your answer.

You can solve many equations by operating on the symbols. In Problem 4.1, the equation for bid 1 is $y = 100 + 4x$, where y is the cost and x is the number of books printed.

To find out how many books can be printed for $300, you can solve the equation $300 = 100 + 4x$ for the variable x.

In your earlier mathematics work, you learned that to solve linear equations such as $300 = 100 + 4x$, you need to *undo* the mathematical operations until x is alone on one side of the equation.

To make sure the sides of the equation remain equal, you must apply any mathematical operation to *both* sides. This *symbolic method* of solution is illustrated below.

$$300 = 100 + 4x$$

$$300 - 100 = 100 - 100 + 4x$$

Since 100 is added to $4x$, subtract 100 from *both sides* of the equation.

$$200 = 4x$$

$$\frac{200}{4} = \frac{4x}{4}$$

Since x is multiplied by 4, divide *both sides* by 4.

$$50 = x$$

Now x is alone on one side of the equation. It is easy to see that the solution is 50. This means that 50 books can be printed for $300.

The example below shows one way to solve the equation
$100 + 4x = 25 + 7x$.

$$100 + 4x = 25 + 7x$$
$$100 + 4x - 4x = 25 + 7x - 4x \qquad 1.$$
$$100 = 25 + 3x$$
$$100 - 25 = 25 + 3x - 25 \qquad 2.$$
$$75 = 3x$$
$$\frac{75}{3} = \frac{3x}{3} \qquad 3.$$
$$25 = x$$

A. Supply an explanation for each numbered step in the above solution to $100 + 4x = 25 + 7x$.

B. The solution above begins by subtracting $4x$ from both sides of the equation. Show a solution that begins with a different step.

C. How can you check that $x = 25$ is the correct solution? Show that your method works.

In A–D, use the symbolic method to solve the equation.

A. $7x + 15 = 12x + 5$

B. $14 - 3x = 1.5x + 5$

C. $-3x + 5 = 2x - 10$

D. $3 + 5(x + 2) = 7x - 1$

E. Check your solutions to the equations in A–D.

F. Look over your work for A–D. Record any general strategies that seem to work well in solving linear equations.

Finding the x-intercepts of the graph of $y = x^2 + 5x$ is the same as solving the equation $x^2 + 5x = 0$.

In earlier units, you solved quadratic equations by using tables and graphs. For example, to solve $x^2 + 5x = 0$, you can trace a graph of $y = x^2 + 5x$ to find x values for which $y = 0$. Or you can make a table of values and look for the x values that correspond to a y value of 0.

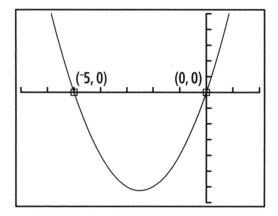

x	y
‾7	14
‾6	6
‾5	**0**
‾4	‾4
‾3	‾6
‾2	‾6
‾1	‾4
0	**0**
1	6
2	14
3	24

The solutions to $x^2 + 5x = 0$ are called the **roots** of the equation $y = x^2 + 5x$. A quadratic equation may have zero, one, or two roots. If r is a root of an equation, then the point $(r, 0)$ is an x-intercept of the graph.

A. The expression $x^2 + 3x$ is in expanded form. Write an equivalent expression in factored form.

B. Find all possible solutions to the equation $x^2 + 3x = 0$. Explain how you know you have found all the solutions.

C. What are the x-intercepts of $y = x^2 + 3x$? Explain how your answers to part B can help you answer this question.

D. Which form of the expression $x^2 + 3x$, the expanded form or the factored form, is more useful for finding the roots, or x-intercepts, of the equation $y = x^2 + 3x$? Explain your reasoning.

E. In 1 and 2, an equation is given for both the factored form and the expanded form of a quadratic expression. Find the roots, or *x*-intercepts, of the equation without making a table or a graph, and tell which form of the equation you used to find your answer.

1. $y = 4x^2 - 8x$ or $y = 4x(x - 2)$

2. $y = 6x(5 - 2x)$ or $y = 30x - 12x^2$

F. In 1–3, solve the equation by first factoring the quadratic expression.

1. $x^2 + 4.5x = 0$

2. $x^2 - 9x = 0$

3. $-x^2 + 10x = 0$

You will need four to six rods of the same length and several unit rods. In this problem, you will find the surface area of stacks of the longer rods. The rods in each stack should be staggered by 1 unit, as shown below.

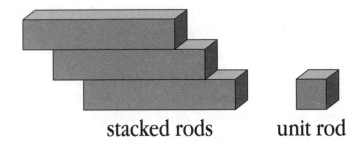

stacked rods   unit rod

A. Use the unit rods to determine the dimensions of one of the longer rods.

B. Find the surface area of a single rod, a stack of two rods, a stack of three rods, and so on.

C. Use your findings to help you write an equation for the relationship between the surface area, *A*, and the number of rods in the stack, *N*.

Dear Family,

The next unit that your child will be studying in mathematics class this year explores the topic that beginning algebra used to focus on almost exclusively: the use of symbols. When you first began studying algebra, you probably spent most of your time learning to manipulate symbols. Chances are you didn't get a chance to think about what the symbols actually meant in terms of the real world. This mathematics curriculum emphasizes the *meaning* behind the symbols. This helps students to build their own understanding of the basics of algebra and its usefulness for solving everyday problems.

Say It with Symbols focuses on the distributive property, which demonstrates a relationship between multiplication and addition. A good understanding of this relationship will take your child a long way in making sense of algebraic symbols. Students will also be reviewing what they have learned about linear and quadratic relationships and the connections among graphs, tables, and verbal statements. Often, students will find more than one way to represent a solution symbolically. This gives them a reason for developing ways to show that some algebraic expressions that look different are actually the same.

Here are some strategies for helping your child during this unit:

- Talk with your child about the situations that are presented and why we can rearrange symbols as shown in the unit.

- Ask your child to show you a problem that can be represented by more than one algebraic expression. Have your child demonstrate that the expressions are actually the same and what they mean in terms of the problem.

- Talk with your child about the importance of being skillful in algebra.

- Encourage your child's efforts in completing all homework assignments.

As always, if you have any questions or suggestions about your child's mathematics program, please feel free to call.

Sincerely,

Estimada familia,

La próxima unidad que su hijo o hija estudiará este año en la clase de matemáticas trata sobre lo que anteriormente fue el tema principal y casi exclusivo en los procesos de iniciación al álgebra: el uso de los símbolos. Cuando antes se comenzaba a estudiar álgebra por primera vez, lo normal era pasar la mayoría del tiempo aprendiendo a manejar los símbolos. Y lo más probable era que no se presentara ninguna oportunidad para pensar en lo que realmente significaban los mismos con relación al mundo real. En cambio, en este programa de matemáticas se destaca la importancia del significado de los símbolos. Esto ayudará a los alumnos a aumentar tanto sus propios conocimientos sobre las nociones básicas del álgebra como sobre la utilidad de ésta para resolver problemas de la vida diaria.

Say It with Symbols (Díselo con Símbolos) trata principalmente sobre la propiedad distributiva, la cual demuestra una relación entre la multiplicación y la adición. Su hijo o hija, cuando llegue a entender bien dicha relación, habrá dado un paso decisivo hacia la comprensión de los símbolos algebraicos. Además de esto, los alumnos repasarán lo aprendido sobre las relaciones lineales y cuadráticas y sobre las conexiones existentes entre gráficas, tablas y enunciados verbales. Es frecuente que consigan encontrar más de una manera de representar una solución mediante símbolos. Así tendrán un motivo para desarrollar caminos alternativos que muestren que algunas expresiones algebraicas aparentemente diferentes son en realidad iguales.

He aquí algunas estrategias que ustedes pueden emplear para ayudar a su hijo o hija en esta unidad:

- Comenten con él o ella las situaciones presentadas y las razones por las que los símbolos pueden colocarse de distintas formas, como puede verse en la unidad.

- Pídanle que les muestre un problema que pueda representarse por más de una expresión algebraica. Díganle que demuestre que en realidad dichas expresiones son iguales y cuál es su significado con relación al problema.

- Comenten juntos la importancia de dominar las técnicas del álgebra.

- Anímenle a esforzarse para que complete toda la tarea.

Y como de costumbre, si ustedes tienen alguna duda o recomendación relacionada con el programa de matemáticas de su hijo o hija, no duden en llamarnos.

Atentamente,

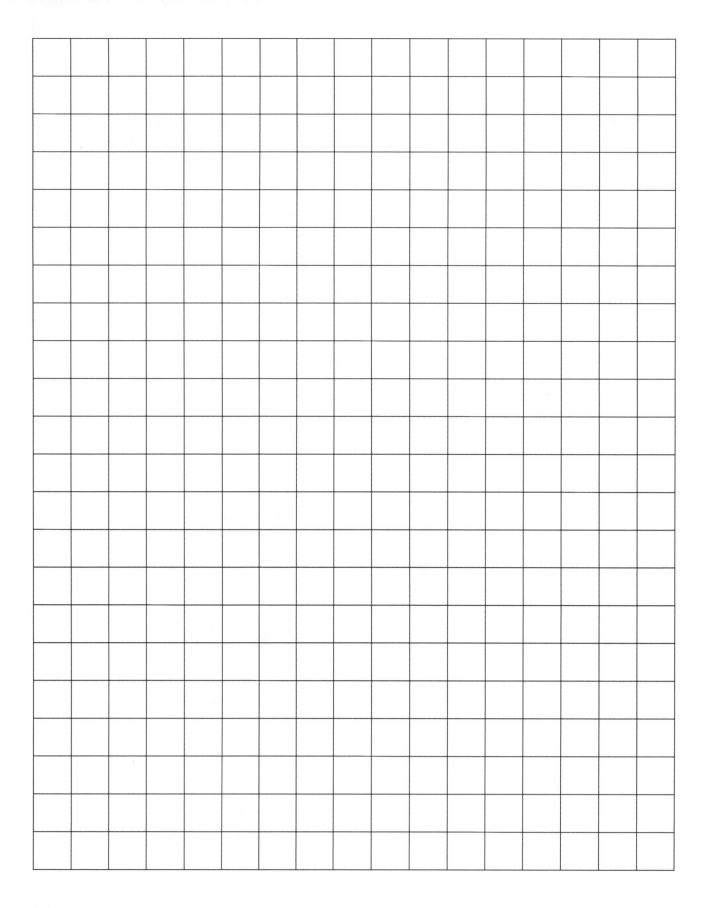

Additional Practice

Investigation 1

Use these problems for additional practice after Investigation 1.

In 1–26, evaluate the expression for the given value of x.

1. $3.5x - 10$ when $x = 2$

2. $45 - 2x$ when $x = 6$

3. $^{-}3 - x$ when $x = \frac{1}{2}$

4. $4x + 9$ when $x = 11$

5. $2x^2$ when $x = 8$

6. $11 - 3x^2$ when $x = 1$

7. $4.5 + x^2$ when $x = 1.5$

8. $6x^2 + 13$ when $x = ^{-}10$

9. $6x^2 + x - 11$ when $x = 2$

10. $6x^2 + x - 11$ when $x = ^{-}2$

11. $12 - 2x^2 + 5x$ when $x = ^{-}4$

12. $12 - 2x^2 + 5x$ when $x = 4$

13. $x(31 - x)$ when $x = 3$

14. $(x + 5)(x - 1)$ when $x = 0$

15. $(x - 1.5)(x + 42)$ when $x = 1.5$

16. $(31 - x)x$ when $x = ^{-}3$

17. $\frac{36}{x^2}$ when $x = ^{-}6$

18. $\frac{x^2}{24}(x + 7)$ when $x = ^{-}7$

19. $42(x + 1)$ when $x = 4$

20. $\frac{3(16 - x)}{2x}$ when $x = 10$

21. $\frac{x}{4} + 6(x - 12)$ when $x = 12$

22. $7x(3 + x)$ when $x = ^{-}4$

23. $7x^2 - x + 10$ when $x = 2$

24. $8x - 2x(6 - x)$ when $x = 0$

25. $0.5x^2 + x - 20$ when $x = 10$

26. $(x + 7)(x - 2)$ when $x = ^{-}5$

27. When Michael and his three friends go to the movies, they each either skate to the theater or ride a bike. The number of wheels in the group as they go to the theater is given by the equation $W = 8s + 2b$, where s is the number of friends skating and b is the number of friends biking.

   a. If Michael decides to skate and his friends decide to bike, how many wheels are in the group?

   b. If everyone decides to skate, how many wheels are in the group?

   c. In the equation $W = 8s + 2b$, explain why the variable s has a coefficient of 8 and the variable b has a coefficient of 2.

   d. Suppose that as Michael and his three friends go to the movies, there are 26 wheels in the group. How many are on skates and how many are riding a bike? Explain how you found your answer.

28. A car is stopped at a red light. When the light turns green, the car begins moving forward. The distance in feet of the car from the light after t seconds is given by the equation $D = 4t^2$.

    a. How far is the car from the light after 5 seconds?

    b. How far is the car from the light after 10 seconds?

    c. How far is the car from the light at $t = 0$ seconds? Explain why your answer makes sense.

29. Susan has a piggy bank into which she puts only nickels. The amount of money in dollars, D, in the bank is given by $D = \frac{n}{20}$, where n is the number of nickels in the piggy bank.

    a. If Susan has 80 nickels in her piggy bank, how many dollars does she have?

    b. If Susan has 94 nickels in her piggy bank, how many dollars does she have?

    c. Based on your answers to parts a and b, explain why the equation makes sense.

Investigation 2

Use these problems for additional practice after Investigation 2.

1. A cube has an edge length of *r*.

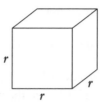

   a. What is the sum of the lengths of all the edges of the cube if *r* = 4?

   b. Write two equations for the sum, *S*, of the lengths of all the edges of a cube with edge length *r*.

2. A rectangular box has length *L*, width *W*, and height *H*.

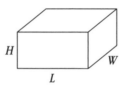

   a. What is the sum of the lengths of all the edges of the box if *L* = 3, *W* = 2, and *H* = 1.5? Show how you found your answer.

   b. Write two equations for the sum, *S*, of the lengths of all the edges of a box with length *L*, width *W*, and height *H*.

The rectangle below has length *L* and width *W*. Use the diagram to answer 3–6.

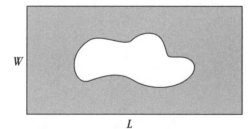

3. Write two equations for the perimeter, *P*, of the rectangle.

4. Suppose the length of the rectangle is equal to twice the width, or 2*W*.

   a. If the width of the rectangle is 1.5, what is the length?

   b. If the width is 2, what is the perimeter?

   c. Write two equations for the perimeter of the rectangle, *P*, in terms of only the width, *W*.

5. If $L = 14$ meters and $W = 6.5$ meters, what is the area of the shaded region inside the rectangle if the area of the blob is 38 square meters? Show how you found your answer.

6. Write an equation for the area, A, of the shaded region inside the rectangle if the area of the blob is Q.

Investigation 3

Use these problems for additional practice after Investigation 3.

1. **a.** Write 45 as a product of two factors.

    b. Write 45 as a product of three factors.

    c. Write 45 as a product of two factors, such that one factor is the sum of two terms.

    d. Write $45x$ as a product of two factors.

    e. Write $45x$ as the sum of three terms.

    f. Write $45x$ as a product of two factors, such that one factor is the sum of two terms, in at least two ways.

In 2–5, rewrite the statement with a number or an expression in each blank to make the statement true.

2. $\underline{}(6 + \underline{}x) = 6x + 18$

3. $\underline{}(8 - 2) = \underline{}x$

4. $3x(3 + \underline{}) = 10x$

5. $11(\underline{} + 3\underline{}) = 33x - 11$

In 6–9, write two expressions that are equivalent to the given expression.

6. $7(x - 4)$

7. $x(5 - 6) + 13x - 10$

8. $2.5(8 - 2x) + 5(x + 1)$

9. $3(x + 10) - 3(2 - 4x)$

In 10–17, write the quadratic equation in factored form.

10. $y = 3x + 21x^2$

11. $q = 72r^2 - 24r$

12. $y = 5x^2 + 10x$

13. $a = 16b - 48b^2$

14. $y = 3(x - 1) + (x - 1)$

15. $y = x^2 + 3x + 2$

16. $y = x(x - 10) + x(2x + 5)$

17. $y = 52x^2 - 13$

18. The Metropolis Middle School volleyball team is operating the concession stand at school basketball games to help raise money for new uniforms. The profit in dollars, P, from operating the stand is given by the equation $P = N - 0.5(\frac{N}{5} + 300)$, where N is the total number of items sold.

    a. How much money will the volleyball team raise if they sell 400 items?

    b. How much money will the volleyball team raise if they sell 550 items?

    c. If the team needs to raise $1000 for new uniforms, will they have to sell more than or fewer than 1000 items? Explain your reasoning.

    d. Write another equation for P.

19. Each side of the figure has length X.

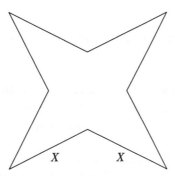

    a. If $X = 3.5$, what is the perimeter of the figure?

    b. If $X = 10$, what is the perimeter of the figure?

    c. Write three equations for the perimeter, P, of the figure.

    d. Show that your three expressions for the perimeter are equivalent.

20. Refer to the figure below to answer a–d.

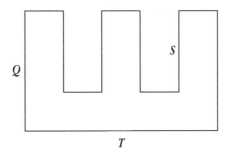

    a. If $Q = 4$ m, $S = 3$ m, and $T = 7$ m, what is the perimeter of the figure?

    b. If $Q = 3$ m, $S = 2.5$ m, and $T = 4$ m, what is the perimeter of the figure?

    c. Using the variables Q, S, and T, write three equations for the perimeter, P, of the figure.

    d. Using the values from part a, find the perimeter of the figure using each of your equations. Check or revise your equations if you do not get the same perimeter in each case.

    e. Show that your three expressions for the perimeter are equivalent.

21. The Metropolis Middle School math and science club is planning to sell crystal-making kits to raise money for new laboratory equipment.

   a. The project will cost $4.50 per kit plus $200 for advertising. Write an equation that represents the cost, C, for k kits.

   b. The students plan to sell each kit for $12 and expect to collect an additional $225 from the kit manufacturer, who will include literature on other science products with each kit. Write an equation that represents the expected revenue, R, from selling k kits.

   c. The profit from selling the kits will be the money left after the students have deducted the cost of the kits from the revenue they collect. Write an equation that represents the profit, P, from selling k kits.

   d. How many kits will the students have to sell to break even (that is, have a profit of zero)? Explain your reasoning.

   e. How many kits will the students need to sell to raise $500?

   f. What will the profit from selling the kits be if the students sell 250 kits?

   g. How many kits will the students need to sell to raise $750?

Investigation 4

Use these problems for additional practice after Investigation 4.

In 1–10, solve the equation and check your answer.

1. $2x + 5 = 11$

2. $9 + 3x = 30$

3. $4x + 19 = 26 - 3x$

4. $x^2 - 2.5x = 0$

5. $11x - x^2 = 0$

6. $5x^2 - 2x = x^2 - 10x$

7. $3x(x - 5) = 0$

8. $4.5(x + 1) + 2(x + 1) = 0$

9. $4.5x = x - 7$

10. $81x - 9x^2 = 0$

11. At right is a graph of a parabola.

    a. What are the coordinates of the maximum
        or minimum point?

    b. What are the coordinates of the x-intercept(s)?

    c. What are the coordinates of the y-intercept(s)?

    d. Could $y = -(x - 4)^2 + 2$ be the equation of
        the parabola? Explain why or why not.

    e. Could $y = x - 2$ be the equation of the
        parabola? Explain why or why not.

    f. Does the line $y = -6$ intersect the parabola?
        Explain why or why not.

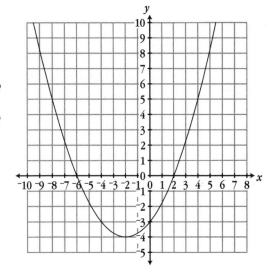

12. The profit, P, from a car wash held by the Metropolis Middle School band depends on the number of cars,
    C, that drive by the corner where the car wash is operated. Past experience suggests that the equation
    modeling the situation is approximately $P = 0.001C(C - 5)$.

    a. What profit can be expected if 100 cars drive by?

    b. What profit can be expected if 1000 cars drive by?

    c. What profit can be expected if no cars drive by? Explain why the profit predicted by the equation does
        or does not make sense.

    d. The band director estimates from past car washes that about 750 cars will drive by during the time the
        car wash is open. The band needs $700 to fund a trip to the state competition. About how many times
        will they have to hold the car wash to raise the necessary funds? Explain your reasoning.

13. The height in meters of a model rocket t seconds after it is launched is approximated by the equation $b = t(50 - 3t)$.

   a. How high is the rocket 5 seconds after being launched?

   b. How high is the rocket 10 seconds after being launched?

   c. Based on your answers to parts a and b, did the rocket's height continue to increase after the first 5 seconds? Explain your reasoning.

   d. What is the height of the rocket after 17 seconds? What can you conclude from your answer? Explain your reasoning.

14. At Metropolis Middle School, the number of cans, N, collected for recycling after a basketball game depends on the number of people, P, who attend the game. The approximate relationship is given by $N = 2.5(P - 40) - 100$.

   a. Is the relationship between the number of cans collected and the number of people attending linear or quadratic? Explain.

   b. If 400 people attended the game for the semifinals of the district championship, how many cans would you expect to be collected?

   c. If 300 cans were collected at a game, how many people would you expect to have attended the game?

   d. If 675 cans were collected at another game, how many people would you expect to have attended that game?

15. The cost, C, of each uniform for the players on an N-person basketball team is given by the equation $C = \frac{(40N + 260)}{N}$.

   a. If there are 25 players on the team, what is the cost of each uniform?

   b. If the cost of each uniform is $53, how many players are on the basketball team?

   c. If the cost of each uniform is $56.25, how many players are on the basketball team?

16. The sum of the length and width of a rectangle is 20 meters. The area of the rectangle is given by the equation $A = w(20 - w)$, where w is the width.

   a. What is the area of the rectangle if the width is 2 meters?

   b. What is the area of the rectangle if the length is 8 meters? Show how you found your answer.

   c. Suppose the area of the rectangle is 75 square meters. What is the width of the rectangle? What is the length of the rectangle?

   d. Suppose the area of the rectangle is 96 square meters. What is the width of the rectangle? What is the length of the rectangle?

   e. What are the dimensions of the rectangle if its area is 93.75 square meters?

Additional Practice

Investigation 5

Use these problems for additional practice after Investigation 5.

1. Toothpicks were used to make the pattern below.

   1st   2nd   3rd   4th

   a. How many toothpicks will be in the 5th figure? In the 6th figure?
   b. Write an equation for the number of toothpicks, *t*, needed to make the *n*th figure.
   c. Identify and describe the figure in this pattern that can be made with exactly 100 toothpicks.

2. Toothpicks were used to make the pattern below.

   1st   2nd   3rd   4th

   a. How many toothpicks will be in the 5th figure? In the 6th figure?
   b. Write an equation for the number of toothpicks, *t*, needed to make the *n*th figure.
   c. Identify and describe the figure in this pattern that can be made with exactly 61 toothpicks.

3. Square tiles were used to make the pattern below.

   1st   2nd   3rd   4th

   a. How many tiles will be in the 5th figure? In the 6th figure?
   b. Write an equation for the number of tiles, *t*, needed to make the *n*th figure.
   c. Identify and describe the figure in this pattern that can be made with exactly 25 tiles.

4. Square tiles were used to make the pattern below.

   1st   2nd   3rd   4th

   a. How many tiles will be in the 5th figure? In the 6th figure?
   b. Write an equation for the number of tiles, *t*, needed to make the *n*th figure.
   c. Identify and describe the figure in this pattern that can be made with exactly 420 tiles.

Investigation 1

1. $^-3$
2. 33
3. $-\frac{7}{2}$
4. 50
5. 128
6. 8
7. 6.75
8. 613
9. 15
10. 11
11. $^-40$
12. 0
13. 84
14. $^-5$
15. 0
16. $^-102$
17. 1
18. 0
19. 210
20. $\frac{9}{10}$
21. 3
22. 28
23. 36
24. 0
25. 40
26. $^-14$

27. **a.** $W = 8(1) + 2(3) = 14$ wheels

    b. $W = 8(4) + 2(0) = 32$ wheels

    c. The 8 represents the number of wheels on a pair of skates, and the 2 represents the number of wheels on a bicycle.

    d. Since $s = 3$ and $b = 1$ is the only way to make W equal to 26, three are on skates and one is riding a bike.

28. **a.** $4(5^2) = 100$ ft

    b. $4(10^2) = 400$ ft

    c. The car is 0 ft from the light because it has not yet begun to move.

29. **a.** $\frac{80}{20} = \$4$

    b. $\frac{94}{20} = \$4.70$

    c. There are 20 nickels in 1 dollar, so the number of nickels divided by 20 gives the number of dollars.

Investigation 2

1. **a.** $12(4) = 48$

    b. $S = 4r + 4r + 4r$ and $S = 12r$

2. **a.** $4(3) + 4(2) + 4(1.5) = 26$

    b. $S = 4L + 4W + 4H$ and $S = 4(L + W + H)$

3. $P = 2L + 2W$ and $P = 2(L + W)$

4. **a.** $L = 2W = 2(1.5) = 3$

    b. $P = 2L + 2W = 2(4) + 2(2) = 12$

    c. $P = 2(2W) + 2W$ and $P = 6W$

5. $14(6.5) - 38 = 53$ m^2

6. $A = WL - Q$

Investigation 3

1. A possible answer is given for each part.

   a. 5×9

   b. $5 \times 3 \times 3$

   c. $9(2 + 3)$

   d. $5(9x)$

   e. $15x + 20x + 10x$

   f. $9x(3 + 2)$ and $3x(10 + 5)$

2. Possible answer: $3(6 + 2x) = 6x + 18$ 3. Possible answer: $x(8 - 2) = 6x$

4. Possible answer: $3x(3 + \frac{1}{3}) = 10x$ 5. Possible answer: $11(^-1 + 3x) = 33x - 11$

6. Possible answer: $7x - 28$ and $\frac{x}{2}(14) - 28$ 7. Possible answer: $12x - 10$ and $2(6x - 5)$

8. Possible answer: 25 and $20 + 5$ 9. Possible answer: $15x + 24$ and $3(5x + 8)$

10. $y = 3x(1 + 7x)$ 11. $q = 24r(3r - 1)$

12. $y = 5x(x + 2)$ 13. $a = 16b(1 - 3b)$

14. $y = 4(x - 1)$ 15. $y = (x + 1)(x + 2)$

16. $y = x(3x - 5)$ 17. $y = 13(4x^2 - 1)$

18. a. $210

    b. $345

    c. Possible answers: They will need to sell more than 1000 items because the equation shows that P is N minus a number. Or, they must sell 1278 items to make a profit of at least $1000.

    d. Possible answer: $P = N - \frac{0.5-}{5} - 150$.

19. a. $8(3.5) = 28$

    b. $8(10) = 80$

    c. $P = 4(2X)$, $P = 8X$, and $P = 2(2X + 2X)$

    d. $P = 4(2X) = 4(2)(X) = 8X$
       $P = 2(2X + 2X) = 2(2)(X + X) = 4(2X) = 8X$

20. a. $2(4) + 4(3) + 2(7) = 34$ m

    b. $2(3) + 4(2.5) + 2(4) = 24$ m

    c. Possible answer: $P = 2Q + 4S + 2T$, $P = 2(Q + T) + 4S$, and $P = 2(Q + T + 2S)$

    d. Answers will vary.

    e. $P = 2(Q + T) + 4S = 2Q + 2T + 4S = 2Q + 4S + 2T$
       $P = 2(Q + T + 2S) = 2Q + 2T + 4S = 2Q + 4S + 2T$

21. **a.** $C = 4.5k + 200$

    b. $R = 12k + 225$

    c. $P = 7.5k + 25$

    d. From $P = 7.5k + 25 = 0$, we can tell that the students can sell no kits and still make $25 (though the kit manufacturer may not want to give them $225 if no kits are sold).

    e. 64 kits

    f. $1900

    g. 97 kits

Investigation 4

1. $x = 3$

2. $x = 7$

3. $x = 1$

4. $x = 0$ or $x = 2.5$

5. $x = 0$ or 11

6. $x = 0$ or $x = ^-2$

7. $x = 0$ or 5

8. $x = ^-1$

9. $x = ^-2$

10. $x = 0$ or $x = 9$

11. **a.** The minimum point is $(^-2, ^-4)$.

    b. $(^-6, 0)$ and $(2, 0)$

    c. $(0, ^-3)$

    d. No; the parabola opens upward, not downward.

    e. No; this is a linear equation.

    f. No; the line $y = ^-6$ is below the minimum point.

12. **a.** $9.50

    b. $995

    c. $0; This makes sense because if no cars drive by, there will be no customers.

    d. The band will raise about $558 per car wash, so they will need to have two car washes.

13. **a.** 175 m

    b. 200 m

    c. Yes, it was higher after 10 s than after 5 s, so the height continued to increase.

    d. According to the equation, the height is $^-17$ m, which means the rocket had already returned to the ground.

14. **a.** linear; It can be simplified to $N = 2.5P - 200$, which is a linear equation of the form $y = mx + b$.

    b. 800 cans

    c. 200 people

    d. 350 people

15. **a.** $50.40

    b. 20 players

    c. 16 players

16. **a.** 36 m^2

    b. When $l = 8$, $w = 20 - 8 = 12$, so $A = 8(12) = 96$ m^2.

    c. width = 15 m, length = 5 m

    d. width = 8 m, length = 12 m

    e. width = 12.5 m, length = 7.5 m

Investigation 5

1. **a.** 5th figure, 16; 6th figure, 19

   b. Possible equation: $t = 3n + 1$

   c. It is the 33rd figure, with 33 squares.

2. **a.** 5th figure, 11; 6th figure, 13

   b. Possible equation: $t = 2n + 1$

   c. It is the 30th figure, with 30 triangles.

3. **a.** 5th figure, 9; 6th figure, 11

   b. Possible equation: $t = 2n - 1$

   c. It is the 13th figure, with 12 tiles extending vertically and 12 tiles extending horizontally from the starting tile.

4. **a.** 5th figure, 30; 6th figure, 42

   b. Possible equation: $t = n(n + 1)$ or $t = n^2 + n$

   c. It is the 20th figure, with a 20 by 20 square and 20 tiles in the arm.

commutative property of addition A mathematical property that states that the order in which quantities are added does not matter. For example, $5 + 7 = 7 + 5$ and $2x + 4 = 4 + 2x$. Sometimes called the *rearrangement property of addition*.

commutative property of multiplication A mathematical property that states that the order in which quantities are multiplied does not matter. For example, $5 \times 7 = 7 \times 5$ and $2x(4) = (4)2x$. Sometimes called the *rearrangement property of multiplication*.

distributive property A mathematical property used to rewrite expressions involving addition and multiplication. The distributive property states that for any three quantities a, b, and c, $a(b + c) = ab + ac$. If an expression is written as a factor multiplied by a sum, the distributive property can be used to multiply the factor by each term in the sum.

$$4(5 + x) = 4(5) + 4(x) = 20 + 4x$$

If an expression is written as a sum of terms and the terms have a common factor, the distributive property can be used to rewrite, or *factor*, the expression as the common factor multiplied by a sum.

$$20 + 4x = 4(5) + 4(x) = 4(5 + x)$$

equivalent expressions Expressions that represent the same quantity, such as $2 + 5$, $3 + 4$, and 7. In this unit, students use the distributive and commutative properties to write equivalent expressions. For example, they can apply the distributive property to $2(x + 3)$ to write the equivalent expression $2x + 6$. By applying the commutative property to $2x + 6$, they can write the equivalent expression $6 + 2x$.

expanded form The form of an expression composed of sums or differences of terms rather than products of factors. The expressions $x^2 + 7x + 12$ and $x^2 + 2x$ are in expanded form.

factored form The form of an expression composed of products of factors rather than sums or differences of terms. The expressions $(x + 3)(x + 4)$ and $x(x - 2)$ are in factored form.

parabola The graph of a quadratic function. A parabola has a line of symmetry that passes through the maximum point if the graph opens downward or through the minimum point if the graph opens upward.

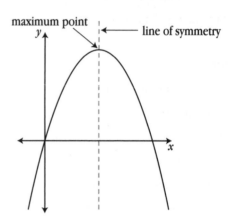

maximum point ← line of symmetry

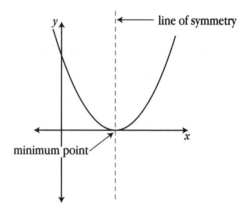

line of symmetry

minimum point

roots The roots of an equation are the values of x that make y equal 0. For example, the roots of $y = x^2 + 5x$ are $^-5$ and 0 because $(^-5)^2 + 5(^-5) = 0$ and $0^2 + 5(0) = 0$. The roots of $y = x^2 + 5x$ are the solutions to the equation $0 = x^2 + 5x$. The roots of an equation are the x-intercepts of its graph.

term An expression with numbers and/or variables multiplied together. In the expression $3x^2 - 2x + 10$, $3x^2$, ^-2x, and 10 are terms.

expresiones equivalentes Expresiones que representan la misma cantidad, como por ejemplo 2 + 5, 3 + 4 y 7. En esta unidad, usaste las propiedades distributiva y conmutativa para escribir expresiones equivalentes. Por ejemplo, puedes aplicar la propiedad distributiva a $2(x + 3)$ para escribir la expresión equivalente $2x + 6$. Mediante la aplicación de la propiedad conmutativa a $2x + 6$, puedes escribir la expresión equivalente $6 + 2x$.

forma de factores La forma de una expresión compuesta de productos de factores en vez de sumas o diferencias de términos. Las expresiones $(x + 3)(x + 4)$ y $x(x − 2)$ están representadas en forma de factores.

forma desarrollada La forma de una expresión compuesta de sumas o diferencias de términos en vez de productos de factores. Las expresiones $x^2 + 7x + 12$ y $x^2 + 2x$ están representadas en forma desarrollada.

parábola La gráfica de una función cuadrática. Una parábola tiene un eje de simetría que pasa por el punto máximo si la gráfica se abre hacia abajo o por el punto mínimo si la gráfica se abre hacia arriba.

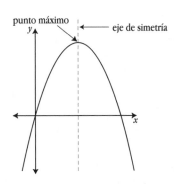

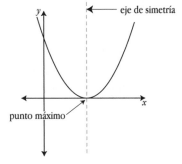

propiedad conmutativa de la multiplicación Una propiedad matemática que dice que el orden en que se multiplican los factores no tiene importancia. Por ejemplo, $5 \times 7 = 7 \times 5$ y $2x(4) = (4)2x$. A veces se la llama *propiedad de reordenamiento de la multiplicación*.

propiedad conmutativa de la suma Una propiedad matemática que dice que el orden en que se suman las cantidades no tiene importancia. Por ejemplo, $5 + 7 = 7 + 5$ y $2x + 4 = 4 + 2x$. A veces se la llama *propiedad de reordenamiento de la suma*.

propiedad distributiva Una propiedad matemática usada para reescribir expresiones que incluyen la suma y la multiplicación. La propiedad distributiva se establece para tres cantidades cualesquiera a, b y c, $a(b + c) = ab + ac$. Si una expresión se escribe como la multiplicación de un factor por una suma, la propiedad distributiva puede usarse para *multiplicar* el factor por cada término de la suma.

$$4(5 + x) = 4(5) + 4(x) = 20 + 4x$$

Si una expresión se escribe como la suma de los términos y los términos tienen un factor común, la propiedad distributiva puede usarse para reescribir o descomponer en factores la expresión como la multiplicación del factor común por una suma.

$$20 + 4x = 4(5) + 4(x) = 4(5 + x)$$

raíces Las raíces de una ecuación son los valores de x que hacen que y equivalga a 0. Por ejemplo, las raíces de $y = x^2 + 5x$ son $^-5$ y 0 porque $(^-5)^2 + 5(^-5) = 0$ y $0^2 + 5(0) = 0$. Las raíces de $y = x^2 + 5x$ son las soluciones de la ecuación $0 = x^2 + 5x$. Las raíces de una ecuación son los puntos de intersección del eje de las x de la gráfica de esa ecuación.

término Una expresión con números y/o variables multiplicados entre sí. En la expresión $3x^2 − 2x + 10$, $3x^2$, ^-2x y 10 son términos.

Index

Index

Index